C000224976

Ghosts of th Morning Shift

An Anthology of Radical Prose from Contemporary Scotland

Edited and Introduced by
Jim Aitken

'... modern history is just beginning... Don't worry, son, others want it beside
yourself. There's not a country in the world where folk aren't striving and
searching. Don't be fooled by the politicians. It isn't the loud men on platforms
but the obscure toilers who change things... ordinary folk will do it and start
the steep upward climb once more.'

—Alasdair Gray (1934-2019), *Lanark*

Culture Matters Co-Operative Ltd. promotes a socialist and progressive approach to art, culture and politics. See www.culturematters.org.uk

Cover painting is 'Ghosts of the Early Morning Shift' by kind permission of the artist, Patrick Donachie
Text is copyright © the contributors
Commissioning editor: Mike Quille
Layout and typesetting by Alan Morrison
ISBN 978-1-912710-40-9

Introduction

By Jim Aitken

Ghosts of the Early Morning Shift is the prose companion volume to *A Kist of Thistles* which came out last year. *Ghosts* is divided into two sections— Memoirs and Flash Fiction with Short Stories. Both anthologies have been produced during the Covid-19 pandemic and will always have a certain level of legacy and importance about them because of this. In this time we have also seen the Tories extend their base further into the North of England, while the SNP won their fourth election victory in a row for Holyrood with one seat short of an overall majority. In Wales it was Labour who won 30 of the 60 seats for the Senned and in Northern Ireland we have seen loyalist rioting, largely brought about through different trading arrangements for Northern Ireland because of the Brexit deal that Johnson secured with the EU.

A Disunited Kingdom

We live in a Disunited Kingdom that the Brexit settlement has further exacerbated. While the electoral facts show a clear political divergence, the cultural impact of all this seems even greater. If Britishness can only equate to monarchy, waving and marketing the Union Jack; the continued denial of our imperial past and its accompanying racism; a class divide with Victorian levels of inequality, together with a punitive welfare system, then it is a union that does not deserve to survive.

Since Johnson's Get Brexit Done election of 2019 Scotland's fishing and farming sector has been well and truly rocked by the more restrictive access to EU markets, and the labour market has plunged since many of the Eastern European workers left, with a devastating impact on our hospitality industry. And hospitality is a key component in a Scotland that has largely become a theme park for tourists.

Most pernicious of all is the new Internal Market Act which will seek to roll back the devolution so hard fought for by the people of Scotland (with the exception of Scottish Tories) and will enable London to bypass Holyrood in distributing its funds to where it can find electoral advantage. Brexit was and is about centralised control—as well as anti-immigration and the racism attached to that. The slogan *Take Back Control*, used during the Brexit referendum of 2016, has an eerie, haunting quality about it when you see who has that control today.

Over the last hundred years Scottish writers, artists and activists have helped to raise the level of cultural awareness, and this has breathed new life into that sense of national consciousness we see today. Alistair Findlay, in

Buried City, tells us that the Scottish literary renaissance of the 1920s has in fact continued to the present day. This ongoing literary and cultural revival has created what we have to call national self-determination. With Scotland last voting for the Tories at a general election in 1955, and inevitably having to accept Tory governments elected by England, this is primarily why there was a Scottish independence referendum in 2014 and why there is now a demand for another one.

Ghosts of the Early Morning Shift is a response, in part, to where we are but also to where we have been. If we do not realise where we have been, we will have little idea about where we may be going. Mairi Murphy considers the notion that *'our past may be our future.'* Or as William Hershaw puts it, in a balletic twist, *'Sometimes you need to birl in order to get back to where you were.'* Scotland has been taking back cultural control this past century and her culture is in exceedingly good shape as a result of this.

The anthology looks back at some of the pioneers of an earlier era and shows how tough it is for some to come to terms with where they have been and where they may be heading. There are some harrowing tales of what living in working-class families and communities can be like, but there are also tales that are uplifting and show solidarity and struggle. The volume does not seek to present a rose-tinted view of Scotland—something that has done so much damage in the past—but to offer a broad and accurate representation of Scotland past and present.

Women in the forefront of struggles

There is also a strong focus on Scottish women by Scottish women, and this reflects how women are in the front line of struggle today. From a figure of 13.2 million trade union members in the UK in 1979, the year Mrs Thatcher came to power, there are only 6.44 million trade unionists today (2020 figures). Of that figure 3.6 million members are women and 2.75 million are men. In Scotland, based on figures for 2019, some 670,000 trade unionists are made up of 32.2% who are women and 26.6% who are men.

Women have often been in the forefront of struggles, and the campaign by 8,000 women in Glasgow employed in homecare, schools and nurseries, cleaning and catering services across the city, took 12 years before the Glasgow City Council equal pay dispute was settled in 2019 in their favour. And even now there are still women from this campaign waiting for their compensation! Low trade union membership is directly responsible for zero hour contracts, chronic low pay and the precarious working environment we have today. This has been engineered that way because it guarantees better profits for owners, and what is called a more competitive economy. If the UK was once dubbed the sick man of Europe in the 1970s, it is a patient on life support today.

The figures of Màiri Mhòr, Helen Crawfurd, Mary Barbour, and Mary Brooksbank remind us how remarkable such women have been to Scotland's story. Their selflessness and desire for better living conditions is in contrast to those who were happy for such appaling conditions to exist in the first place. When reading Catriona Burness on *Mary Barbour* it was difficult not to make a comparison with how Mary organised boxes of fish for the Govan housewives of her day, with the unparalleled use of food banks in our day. What has really changed in a hundred years? It is no coincidence that the first essay is by Bill McKeraghan, a food bank volunteer in Edinburgh.

The fact that we seem to have become accustomed to living with food banks and with homelessness shows the growing irrelevance of a Labour Party that seems bereft of any mission for social justice. When we saw Sir Keir Starmer in a food bank campaigning in the Hartlepool by-election, he was busily putting food into boxes and ticking off items on his checklist. If this image of a Labour leader was meant to show how he cared, then it can only show how utterly out of touch this party has become. Why was he not standing in the food bank to say to the cameras—and to the country—how outraged he was at its existence?

This does not in any way suggest that we do not need food banks but the question must always be raised—why are they so necessary in one of the richest countries in the world? While volunteers like Bill McKeraghan show the decency of many people in wishing to help others, his account shows that he fully expects the need for food banks to grow. Not only that, but with these places now appointing people to full-time paid positions, they are clearly on the way to becoming businesses. And if this trend continues, we will see fundraising to pay for remunerated staff at the expense of those in need.

At the other end of the scale it was reported in March of this year that billionaire Sir Bob Hohn, a hedge fund manager, paid himself £343 million in 2020 after his Children's Investment Fund Foundation had recorded a 66% jump in pre-tax profits. Sir Bob, like so many others in the super-rich category, gives money to charity, but it should also be pointed out that his hedge fund is based in Mayfair and owned by a parent company in the Cayman Islands tax haven.

There you have it—the two faces of Britain. One in need of charity—and does not want to be—and the other known—and knighted—for giving to charity. Wealth on this scale is not only hypocritical, it is corrupt. And we are told today that there is no such thing as class anymore—that, like in America, anyone can make it here. Aye, right.

The cultural struggle

Many will have heard of John Maclean, others will not. There are several biographies of him and one written by Gerard Cairns—*The Red and the Green: A Portrait of John Maclean*. In this anthology Gerard looks at the John Maclean Society that was founded in 1968. What is so significant about this Society is not just that it sought to keep alive the memory of Maclean, but that this attempt itself became a cultural one. The figures that Gerard mentions— Hugh MacDiarmid, Hamish Henderson, Sorley Maclean, Derrick Thomson and other poets, along with figures like Alasdair Gray and Sean Connery and musicians of many hues, together with academics—all of this activity and energy was as much cultural as it was political. And Andy Crichton gives us a short story called *Dominie*, the Scots word for teacher and used by Matt McGinn for his song to Maclean. Crichton seems to have unearthed a story handed down about Annie, once taught by Maclean and allowed to bring him food while he was in jail.

It is the strong cultural input into Scottish politics that has taken us to where we are today. Our cultural sphere in Scotland has traditionally seen itself in the service of the people. It has never been exclusive or remote from them. Mhàiri Mhòr sang about the Gaels, Alistair Hulett sang about Mary Barbour's Army of wonderful women, Mary Brooksbank sang about the poor jute workers of Dundee and Hamish Henderson sang about great John Maclean of the Clyde. Culture has always been deeply embedded in our struggles.

Similarly, David Betteridge brings to life the level of reading that was done by many of the UCS workers and shows their thirst for learning. Both Carlos Arredondo and Zareen Taj Islam show the power that culture has in helping to combat fascism, Islamophobia and racism.

Some of our writers raise the thorny issue of sectarianism. It is a tribute to them that they do. Alistair Findlay looks back at the working-class culture he grew up with and mentions Masonic and Orange lodges. Brian Hamill, in his short story *Donald's Da*, is inventive in creating the figure of Big Don, an agoraphobic bigot who can go and buy his lottery ticket and come out into his garden but can't come out of himself and move away from his ingrained bigotry. And Peter Bennett, in *A Hauf an a Hauf*, takes us into the Portland Arms, an actual pub where there are Celtic and Rangers sections in the bar that have voluntarily been created by the patrons themselves. And John Cassidy, looking back at his apprentice years on the Clyde, tells us he was 'the first Catholic apprentice plater to start in twenty years.'

Findlay says that 'the vast majority of those now living in Scotland' are not religious and by this he implies that Scotland is now largely secular. While this is borne out by census facts it makes it all the more remarkable that there are groups still fighting the Reformation that took place in the 16th century. This is something that blights lives and—literally in some cases —disfigures them. Yet Scotland today is a multicultural country, and even though it is largely secular, there are many Catholics, many other Christians of various persuasions, Muslims, Sikhs, Buddhists, Hindus and Jews, alongside many others, who all contribute to the cultural enrichment of Scottish society. Our parliament in Holyrood is also, at its last intake earlier this year, beginning to reflect this fact.

The poets at the start of Scotland's literary renaissance all felt that Calvinism had a disastrous impact on Scottish culture. MacDiarmid became an atheist, a Communist and a Scottish nationalist, though his work remained littered with Biblical references, and the genial Norman MacCaig variously described himself as both a failed Calvinist and a Zen Calvinist. In a poem of his called *The Kirk*—the name traditionally given to the Church of Scotland— he uses a powerfully Scottish image to describe the God of the Kirk: *'Haven't the people learned yet that God/ is an absentee landlord?'* And in Donald Smith's essay on Hamish Henderson, *Seeing the Voice*, he recalls Hamish talking about *'divesting—in the vestry!'*

It is worth pointing out that another early member of this group, Tom MacDonald, who took the name Fionn MacColla, wrote a powerful critique against Calvinism called *At the Sign of the Clenched Fist* as well as writing novels attacking the Kirk for its complicity in the Highland Clearances. He went on to become a Catholic, as did George Mackay Brown, the Orcadian writer.

The Church of Scotland has seen its membership slump. Numbers of Catholics have also fallen, although its rate of decline is not nearly as severe as that in the Church of Scotland. Why is any of this important? It is important to our writers since there are people who wish to demean others because of their denominational affiliation. Our writers see and hear about this and want to write about it because they wish for a better Scotland, and for that they should be applauded.

Class trumps tribe

Sectarianism seems all the more ludicrous in a society that is largely secular today, though it was entirely welcome to hear Scotland's First Minister call out the Rangers fans who were 'celebrating' their league victory by breaking Covid restrictions in Glasgow's George Square in May this year. She called their behaviour *'vile, anti-Catholic bigotry'*. In a crude way, their behaviour was also a show of their Unionism and their Britishness which, for them, must always equate with Protestantism. And their Protestantism defines itself simply by not being Catholic. Anti-Catholic bigotry is certainly part of their raison d'être but, according to the book *No Problem Here: Understanding Racism in Scotland*, edited by the late Neil Davidson and three of his colleagues from Glasgow University, anti-Catholic bigotry is only one aspect of this form of hatred. The other aspect is anti-Irish racism. People with Irish Catholic backgrounds are on the receiving end of this abuse and it is deeply embarrassing that this persists in a Scotland where most people do not attend any church.

It must also be said that there are bampots in the Celtic support and in Scotland—as in Ireland and elsewhere—terrible tales of clerical abuse and cover-up within the Catholic Church have been exposed. There are no winners for either group when a mass of poor, underprivileged people put so much energy into their team beating the other team while their social conditions continue to worsen. Peter Bennett calls it out accurately—*Ah've seen countless acts ay violence borne frae the ignorance ay bloody eejits oan baith sides ay the fence.*

In David Betteridge's essay on UCS, he mentions many names of stalwarts who led the campaign. Many know about Reid and Airlie, but the name of Sammy Barr is also mentioned by Betteridge. He was a Govan man and the one responsible for the idea of the work-in. He was also a Rangers fan as well as being the Chair of the CPGB. Class always trumped tribe as far as he was concerned and if more fans from all sides remembered this fact then so much the better. Hamish Henderson, in his *The John Maclean March*, sings of all the people all over Scotland coming to welcome Maclean back to Glasgow. In that number he mentions, *'Pat Malone: sure I knew you'd be here so/The red and the green, lads, we'll wear side by side.'* Hamish's song represents the inclusive Scotland he wanted and today I feel sure he would be happy to add the names of Carlos, Zareen and Leela to that list.

Racism, imperialism and toxic masculinity

Racism and imperialism are closely connected. Leela Soma's story *Locked In* is set during British rule in India and it is a devastating riposte to everything that 'Rule Britannia' stands for.

Interestingly, in the essay by Liz Macrae Shaw on Màiri Mhòr, we are told that Màiri was given a cottage to live in rent-free by the landlord, Lachlan MacDonald. He had made his money in India as an indigo and tea planter. She describes him as generous to his tenants, but he would have made his fortune exploiting the labour of Indians in the most dreadful ways imaginable. Leela Soma's story recalls exactly what British imperial rule was about.

Jim Mainland offers a subtle piece of flash fiction entitled *Imperial*. In style this piece is remarkably similar to Beckett's late prose, but where Beckett writes about our existential condition, Mainland's prose enters us into a shadowy world where women are being trafficked. Yet again we realise we have not developed much from earlier times.

What Soma and Mainland have in common thematically, they share with Kathryn Metcalfe's mother in *That Was Just The Women*. Metcalfe recalls her mother campaigning against the opening of a sex shop in Paisley when she was a young girl. She innocently asked her mother *'What does it sell?'* and her mother replied, *'Dirty pictures!'* Clearly, under capitalism—and imperialism, its highest form—everything becomes a commodity to be sold. Tea, jute, indigo, women. Any sex shop anywhere is using sex as a commodity to make profits. What happens to human relationships as a result of this is entirely irrelevant so long as profits are made. What is truly dirty is the enabling of such a dubious trade.

Men who operate in the manner described by Soma, Mainland, and Metcalfe embody toxic masculinity. This theme is mentioned in Carol McKay's biographical details. The stories by John Wight, Des Dillon, Gerda Stevenson, and James Robertson all look at aspects of this. Wight, in *Please, God*, uses the dramatic monologue of a schoolboy on the receiving end of physical and mental abuse at the hands of his parents, particularly his father. Sadly, this is an aspect of working-class life that seems all too prevalent. The father, unable to express his feelings about his job or about his emotions more generally, vents all his anger and frustration against his son. What saves the son, however, from becoming another casualty in the longer term is his final plea to God at the end of the story—*One final thing, God, please dinnae let me turn oot like him.*

In *Ten-Pound Note*, Des Dillon tells the story of a father on his way to see his son in prison. This too is an all too common event in working-class circles. But what goes with the visit is the insistence by the son that no emotion must be shown. If your mother comes to visit you in prison, she must not cry: *'See if your maw cries, ye get a right slagging for it.'* And if your father cries during any visit, we are told *'That's the worst thing that can happen.'* Appearing tough is mandatory in such a culture and relationships are made all the worse because of it. Exactly the same applies to the tough women Metcalfe noted in her own childhood. Later she would realise just how fragile they actually were. It is invariably the same with men who, if they expressed their feelings without anger, could go some way to recovering their lives.

Gerda Stevenson's *Cat Wumman* finds herself in a controlling marriage. Cleverly, in another dramatic monologue, Stevenson prepares her reader well for the ending as the Gran had her misgivings about the marriage. The husband had called his wife his *Pussy Cat* and had gone further still by getting a tattoo of a fierce cat emblazoned on his chest for all to see in honour of her. His demeaning behaviour is eventually confronted and *Cat Wumman* reclaims her freedom in one of the most memorable moments in the anthology.

The bitter fruits of class division

James Robertson's short story *Unsicht* is a translation into Scots of a short story by Guy de Maupassant (1850-1893). Robertson uses a much more extensive Scots vocabulary than others who write in Scots in the anthology, and he shows how high art can come from its use. Maupassant formed part of what was then called in France the Naturalist school of writing, reflecting social forces at the time that produced a myriad of broken lives. Today, we would call it urban realism, though *Unsicht* is set in the countryside.

In the story, a blind man goes to live with his sister once his parents die and he is not given any support or sympathy but exposed instead to merciless cruelties. The level of inhumanity he experiences causes his death, as he is left to fend for himself far from home at the height of a cold winter. It is a truly grim tale but one that raises a few questions for us. Because he cannot sell any labour, he is seen as a problem, a burden. But more than this, others who must labour to eke a living for themselves have become brutalised by their condition and, in turn, brutalise others like the blind man. This was the nature of society in late 19th century France and it has a certain resonance with the conditions many have to endure in our day. The *Unsicht* of the blind man is really the *Unsicht* of the society that pushes down its economic brutality to those at the bottom. Their brutalities, invariably enacted upon each other, reflect the brutal nature of society itself. These are the bitter fruits of class division—then and now.

Kindness, humanity and compassion

We see this in a delicately written story by A.C. Clarke, *A Small Packet of Tissues*. The writer is standing at a bus stop when a young man arrives with his nose bleeding profusely. It turns out he was attacked by other lads he did not know—and this is a common event in our towns and cities. But where the family and others show no sympathy to the blind man of *Unsicht*, the writer offers the bleeding teenager *'a small packet of tissues which would be soaked through in no time'*.

This simple act of kindness brings to mind Ralph Waldo Emerson, who said, *'You cannot do an act of kindness too soon because you never know how soon it will be too late.'* Just as A.C. Clarke has risen above the level of indifference too many people show to others, sound political understanding can also raise people up. When we recall the famous speech of Reid to the UCS workers: *'There will be no hooliganism, there will be no vandalism, there will be no bevvying'*, he was effectively saying, *'There will be no toxic masculinity.'*

If we add in the word *'bevvying'* to the mix we end up with a drunken, violent father as in Wight's *Please, God* and have a probable reason why the son in Dillon's *Ten-Pound Note* has ended up in prison. Carol McKay gives us a disturbing insight into alcoholism in *Under Cadzow Bridge* and she shows the disorientation of mind that comes with such an addiction. There is nothing funny about alcohol, least of all in families that are poor.

The act of kindness that Mary McCabe shows to Gary in *Doon the Careers Office* is on another level almost amusing. She cleverly uses pauses in her text to show that she is thinking how best to help out the forlorn Gary and captures the sense of the interview as it must have happened. People who work in such places also seek to raise people up. This, of course, is what our nurses and doctors have been doing so valiantly this last year and it was gratifying to have a memoir from a former nurse, Mairi Murphy, in her appropriately titled *Shift*.

Kindness and brutality are the dialectical twins. Kindness by others keeps everything from sinking that bit further down the scale. But the level of brutality that the state can show to others it considers 'illegal' or 'alien' is of a different level of brutality entirely. Both Andrew O'Hagan and Jean Rafferty take this on in another two dramatic monologues that overlap particularly well.

O'Hagan's narrator is a nurse, and she is recognisable to anyone— she is caring, garrulous, talks with a west coast, working-class accent. On her way to work she sees a naked man lying next to a skip. Clearly, O'Hagan is suggesting the man is similar to the rubbish that would normally be dumped there. Or *'a mere social cipher'* as his quote from Balzac would have it. The naked man is eventually taken to the Queen Elizabeth Hospital. As the nurse seeks to find out how the man is, she is coldly told by the consultant, 'He's a transitional nobody.' Furthermore, the man is said to be 'not our problem'. While the nurse narrates the story in her Scots voice, these two comments in English are made to be all the more powerful and chilling. These comments are the comments of a callous state.

Jean Rafferty's *Didn't She Matter?* is a story that is a variation on the real-life story of Mercy Baguma, who died in a flat in Govan in August of last year with her malnourished child in his cot. Rafferty names her Blessing in her tale, which shows the writer's magnanimity to her character since the UK state showed the poor woman little in the way of mercy when she lived here. She was a blessing but was treated as an alien, a problem, as someone other.

What Rafferty does is to render Blessing fully human, with a Ugandan hinterland that was in no way impoverished in the way that she lived here. Her narrator is Grace, her sister, and it was Mercy's sister Sarah who wanted no politicisation of her sister's tragedy to be done. Rafferty shows how the writer can respond with decency and tact to what was a horrifying incident of state neglect, while also revealing the strength of her own outrage as well as her humanity.

And humanity is key to all the pieces in this anthology. Hershaw rails against Thatcherism as Allan Armstrong rails against the British state as the entity responsible for most of our problems. Honor Pringle, in a short memoir, recalls an incident from her childhood that is now an act of atonement on her part for having written about a man called Willie. And Geraldine Gould brings back to life two older women who seem unnoticed now but who lived interesting lives that were once vibrant and full of passion.

A good number of our writers use Scots and Sophie Parke, exiled in Oxford, looks back fondly to her Glasgow days clubbing and offers a love letter to the Glaswegian dialect. She captures all the irreverence and gallusness we associate with this great city. However, it is pretty certain that John Maclean, Mary Barbour, and Helen Crawfurd—maybe Kathryn Metcalfe's mother too —would not have approved of her language. One hundred years on from Maclean, Barbour, and Crawfurd, attitudes have changed considerably. Parke's love for the city of her birth is genuine and there can be no problem with that. If anything, love letters to the many other dialects of Scotland would seek to challenge Parke with their own distinctive levels of irreverence.

Tom Hubbard pays a generous homage to his *Grandads*. They helped form the person he has become with the thoughtful, eclectic mind he has. He brings them back to life in all their decency and humanity. Coinneach Maciver, however, shows the Scottish roots of someone we would maybe not wish to acknowledge while remaining proud of Coinneach for telling us his absorbing tale about Mary and Christina Ann. And Vikki Carpenter, maybe most important of all, reminds us what this last year has been like for mums like her. She says she Cannae Complain but she must have had her moments to contend with. It would be wonderful if, in years to come, her children or grandchildren to come can look back on her selflessness and courage at a time of great anxiety and pay tribute to her as Tom Hubbard has to his *Grandads*.

It is important to thank a few people who have made this anthology possible. A.C. Clarke of the Federation of Writers (Scotland), Jean Rafferty of Dove Tales, and Mary McCabe of Scottish PEN all helped to publicise the callout for the book. Also Audrey Canning, Meg Bateman, and Steve Byrne helped provide me with contact addresses for some of our writers. Thanks also to Linda Somerville, Deputy General Secretary of the STUC, for providing me with trade union membership figures.

Pat Donachie, the Dundee artist, has kindly allowed us to use his painting *Ghosts of the Early Morning Shift* for both the front cover and the title of the book. His painting shows a group of shawled women heading to Cox's Mill in Dundee to start their shift. The jute they worked with, of course, came from British imperial India. One of them could easily have been Mary Brooksbank, while others would have been Irish immigrants along with women cleared from Skye by Lord MacDonald. It is a painting that tells many stories about Scotland.

Thanks also to Mark Penrose for his illustration to Carol McKay's *Under Cadzow Bridge* and for his other illustration *Low Wage*, and to Andy Crichton for his own illustration to his story, *Dominie*. Andy would like to thank Frank Docherty for his assistance with this illustration. Bob Starrett must be thanked for both his Hamish Henderson illustration and for his hugely significant illustration of the briar. And thanks to Peter Long for his illustration to Jim Mainland's *Imperial*. Thanks also to Catriona Burness and the Remember Mary Barbour Association for the use of their photograph at the unveiling of the Mary Barbour statue on International Women's Day at Govan Cross, 2018. And thanks to Camilo Arredondo for allowing me to contact his father, Carlos.

Where are we going?

It is impossible to know where Scotland may be heading. Maybe towards independence, maybe not—it is certainly a fascinating country to be living in at this moment. Wherever she may be heading, she is going to have to be like David Betteridge's briar, digging down deep with her roots and seeking all the necessary alliances required to grow towards something greater. And there simply has to be something that is better than this Tory Brexit we are living in now, which seems more like a Greater England than any union of four nations. Scotland never voted for Brexit and has never voted Tory for almost 70 years!

This, in essence, is the democratic deficit that fuels the demand for another independence referendum. Only by digging deep can we hope to locate all those in need of new growth. Hamish Henderson dug deep roots with the Traveller community, an often reviled section of society, and made alliances that are now part of Scotland's rich cultural heritage. Allan Armstrong has been digging away for 40 years and is probably on to his fifth or sixth spade by now. All these writers reveal the importance of reaching out further than ever before; of inspiring others who have been neglected, felt buried or taken for granted; and of raising up both our people and our nation— particularly the beleaguered working class of our nation.

Our writers have written about people in the past and have created characters in the here and now. In a certain way the people they write about are all ghosts, either because they are no longer living or because they are imaginary—yet they can still talk to us, haunt us and prick our conscience. There is a vitality about all the characters evoked, past and present. That is a tribute entirely to the writers of *Ghosts of the Early Morning Shift*.

Edinburgh,
May 2021.

Contents

Memoirs

Flash Fiction and Short Stories

Memoirs

'Emulate the briar, digging down deep with your sustenance-seeking roots, and climb high towards future's light, spiralling up and up, following a trajectory similar to Tatlin's Tower, making sure that your older, jaggier shoots support the younger ones'.

—David Betteridge, 'Rediscovering the Best Part: UCS at 50'

'She undoubtedly challenged the status quo of her day, taking on the landlords and the power of the state in wartime. She wanted not only to change but to revolutionise living conditions'.

—Catriona Burness, 'Mary Barbour'

'The clinging to capitalism, the ownership of the world by a small propertied class, is driving the people of this planet swiftly along the path to perdition'.

—John Maclean, 'Election Address, Glasgow 6 November 1923'

Bill McKeraghan

is originally from Rosyth in Fife. He grew up in a working-class family of six and went on to become a chartered engineer. He graduated from Heriot-Watt University after a four-year sponsored course with Scottish Gas. In 1976 he received his first assignment in the International Energy and Processing Industry. He spent the rest of his working life in project management in overseas locations. These included Western and Central Europe, North and South Africa, the Middle East and India. Pre-Brexit, Bill became a volunteer with the Edinburgh Food Project. He lives now in Edinburgh.

Reflections of a Food Bank Volunteer

Little did I realise, growing up in a working-class family of six in a subsidised house in Rosyth, with wartime rationing and subsequent food restrictions, that such experiences would instil in me values that would be appreciated in later life. Such values that understood the place of having a secure home, free state schooling, frugality, basic economics and the balance between necessity, wants and luxuries. And this childhood also created the delicate balance between ambition, opportunity and the rewards of hard work despite coming from what many may regard as a disadvantaged background.

Despite our financial constraints, there was never a need to seek assistance from food banks. Indeed, I have no recollection of them from these early years. In fact, at that time, there was support given to Scottish working-class families like mine at both local and national levels, which enabled me to achieve both a professional career at an international level and to have a fulfilled life.

While enjoying the challenges of living overseas in what became known as third world countries, my wife and I experienced a wide spectrum of experiences, especially in relation to poverty and food shortage. Living in a remote village (same population as Edinburgh!) in northern India showed us the values of simplicity, scarcity and maximising the greatest use of available food. Meg had to spend a large portion of her day developing the skills of buying from street markets, sterilising all fruits and vegetables, and cooking from scratch without recourse to modern appliances. We did have a freezer, which was primarily used to store bulk flour and ensure the separation of the dead weevils before bread making. This latter activity was therapeutic, as pounding the dough helped eliminate any frustrations.

At this time, with the help of a financial donation from our faith family in The Hague, Meg was able to provide the local high school nuns with the cash to purchase quantities of staples, have the pupils make them up into food packs and distribute these packs to impoverished street dwellers.

On returning to Scotland after an absence of 35 years it was clearly a different country to the one we left all those years ago. Polarisation and political rancour were self-evident together with the overt increase in poverty, charity shops and food banks. Driven by the fact that I was fit, healthy and determined to repay society the benefits I had received, I investigated various charitable options before settling for the Trussell Trust food bank in Edinburgh. This one was not only nearest to me, but it was governed by an ethos that aligned well with my own thoughts.

Historically, this enterprise had been established several years previously by a young man, his family and a small group of his faith members. Initially converting his garage into an office and storage facility, he pioneered what has now grown considerably into the Edinburgh Food Project (EFP). From this small beginning the EFP has expanded to meet the ever-increasing demands for food in Scotland's capital city.

Edinburgh is internationally renowned for its historic heritage, its classical architecture, art galleries and annual arts festivals. It is also a centre of banking and commerce with a multitude of extremely expensive properties. However, it is also a city where the level of food poverty, even prior to Covid-19, affects 20% of the population with one third of that number being children.

EFP is merely one of many charitable organisations established in the city to alleviate food poverty and the EFP supplies approximately 50% of these needs. To try to address the growing level of food poverty and the additional societal needs over the 5-year period I have been associated with EFP, it has now expanded into 2 permanent offices and associated storage facilities with additional rental space for peak times. These facilities service 8 distribution centres strategically located from South Queensferry in the North-West through the city centre out to Craigmillar in the East.

Staff numbers, volunteers and employees have grown to ensure that those in need are catered for. Over 200 volunteers, 1 full-time director and 5 employees support staff to fulfil the many important tasks and logistics that make the system run as smoothly as possible. Apart from the obvious tasks of receiving donations, dating them, segregation and storage prior to then making up food parcels, a whole organisation is required to maintain distribution to needy people. This involves ensuring that transport is available as well as fulfilling important administrative requirements.

Over the recent period from April until September 2020, there has been an increase of 47% in need compared to what was supplied over the same period in 2019. This has resulted in 17,000 3-day emergency food parcels distributed over that period to people in crisis.

Due to lockdown restrictions, the 'modus operandi' of EFP has had to be drastically curtailed. Distribution centres have had to be closed and there has been a reduction in warehouse staffing too. Instead of 5 separately sized food packs, food parcels are now rationalised into a single box which then forms a modular basis for supplying different sized families and their requirements. All these requirements are requisitioned electronically from referral agencies, some 200 of whom are signed up to the EFP, and deliveries are now made to the homes of those in desperate need by volunteers as required.

The rise in demand for EFP services in the 5 years I have had the privilege of working with them can be traced to the social and economic changes being meted out to our poorest people. It is a matter of public record that measures such as zero-hour contracts, Universal Credit, the downturn in the UK economy with concomitant layoffs have all contributed to a worsening social situation. It should also be said that pre-Brexit delays in private sector investment and relocation of businesses outside the UK have contributed to the rise in food poverty throughout Scotland and the rest of the UK. The blow to the economy and reduction in income for many households has only reinforced the necessity for food banks. There are not infrequent cases of working families on low incomes who have to resort to benefits and food parcels, as well as staff being laid off at short notice and waiting for benefits to come through.

The quality and dedication of the staff and volunteers is incredible, as is the generosity of the public. The supermarkets also provide both material and physical resources, enabling the EFP to keep up with these ever-increasing demands. Without such support it is unthinkable what tragic outcomes could result. Many of the volunteers are older people, like myself, who are thankful for our relative security but are motivated simply to try to lessen the misery in our midst.

Volunteers are an amazing group of people of all ages, skills, experiences and life-styles but bonded by one common attribute of caring and trying to make, albeit in a small way, a difference by giving back what we have been fortunate to receive. Ages range from the traditional '3 score and 10' (in some cases, surpassing), down through to teenagers. Proficiency levels include retired engineers, administrators, teachers, civil servants, as well as people from all trades and occupations. There are some who currently work shifts or part-time but are happy to give up their free time to assist. There have been young people looking for work experience as well as others seeking to achieve national awards in recognition of public services.

Also welcomed into the operation at the warehouse are people who have health challenges which can be barriers to regular employment. There is one young man who has communication difficulties but he is a whizz-kid at inputting and transferring information into the database. He is the fastest on the admin team. Another young man who, with his carer, is happy to make up individual packs of sugar, tea, etc. from bulk, provided we can supply him with Irn-Bru which is an exception to the policy of not issuing soda drinks high in sugar!

Being motivated to volunteer for this work, although I was initially a touch apprehensive, I have been rewarded and blessed by the level of appreciation that exists in the wider world. It is so rewarding to receive unsolicited phone calls from people offering to make donations or to volunteer. And there have been so many heart-warming incidents: from the elderly, who having worked out their own needs, decide to send a cheque or food donation, even though they are in receipt of Winter Fuel Allowance; school children who have gone out shopping with their own pocket money to purchase items for young people; the woman at Waverley station who quietly placed a large note in my collection box while expressing her appreciation for the help she had once received herself; the elderly Polish man who expressed his appreciation of the parcel I had given him at one of our distribution centres, not in English but with a hug; the toddler who came rushing up to me at a supermarket collection and handed over her favourite chocolate bar for some less fortunate child at Christmas; the dad who rang relating how his young daughter had called on an elderly neighbour who had been shielding and had not eaten much more than a plate of porridge recently and who arranged for her to receive regular social worker visits and a food parcel.

The largest, by far, majority of callers looking for help or general information are all incredibly grateful and thankful. On the other hand, there have been moments of sadness and frustration when taking calls from people who are desperately in need, not just of food parcels, but who do not know how to make contact with the agencies that can help them with their other needs.

However, thanks to the foresight of the staff and Trustees in recognising that the supply of emergency food parcels did not cater for the extensive needs of some people, a great deal of time and effort has gone into restructuring the organisation so that these needs are met.

Food parcel contents have been expanded to include other domestic essentials. These additional items include personal and household hygiene products such as shower materials, shaving items, toothpaste, deodorants, cleaning items, nappies, and sanitary products.

Recognising that food parcels were merely a plaster, decisions were made to upgrade the quality of care for those in greatest need. With the selection of highly qualified and highly driven individuals, our scope has been extended to include services offering debt management and advice on how to file claims for benefits that claimants are entitled to. This has been particularly acute for those people who have found themselves in dire circumstances for the first time. The EFP now liaises with many outside organisations, both private and public. This work has become particularly important with regard to many people who now require assistance with mental health problems.

As a result, in the growth of EFP there was the need to appoint a manager, not only for the 200 or more volunteers who work at all the food banks, warehouses, and offices, but also to organise all the collection drives. And someone had to oversee warehouse storage, transport and distribution.

As with most other charities, EFP, although within the Trussell Trust umbrella, is a charity in its own right and is therefore responsible for its financial security. A recent appointment has seen this person tasked with looking after grant applications, financial reporting to the Trustees, interfacing with Trussell Trust as well as looking after the financial donations received on a daily basis. There is also the need to plan general administration to ensure the necessary documentation is met and recorded.

So much for the past and present. What about the future?

The EFP has grown from small beginnings into a well-structured and highly focussed organisation, flexible enough to rise to the constantly changing needs of Edinburgh's underprivileged population. It is capable of being not only a self-contained unit, though dependent on support and contributions to complete its task, but is well established with outside organisations to offer a far broader approach to the poor in the city.

How long will the current need for this charity last? Clearly for some time in the foreseeable future. Naturally it would be better if there were no need for food banks at all, but until that day comes there will continue to be dedicated people helping to alleviate the suffering of the poor. And for myself, once lockdown is lifted, I intend to volunteer once again.

Alistair Findlay

is a poet and editor, author of *Sex, Death & Football, Dancing with Big Eunice* and the social work memoir *Mollycoddling the Feckless*. With Tessa Ransford he co-edited the anthology *Scotia Nova: Poems for the Early Days of a Better Nation. Lenin's Gramophone: Scotland's Left Poetry and Song 1865-1990s* is forthcoming from Luath Press, from where all his books are available.

Buried City

George Ogilvie was the 16-year-old Christopher M Grieve's English teacher at Broughton Academy, Edinburgh, in 1908, who encouraged him to fulfil his writing ambitions like many another bright working-class youngster. Grieve became Hugh MacDiarmid a dozen years later, the greatest Scottish poet and cultural activist since Robert Burns.

The role Ogilvie played was not unusual in early 20th century Scotland's education system in which the 19th century lad o' pairts tradition continued unabated. Local teachers and dominies talent-spotted gifted working-class lads (not lassies) guiding them to university, to the extent that by the 1860s they comprised nearly a quarter of the student body.

The socialist movement created a similar radical version of this over the same period, the self-taught autodidactic tradition which produced working-class socialist and labour movement activists who read all kinds of literature—from Burns, Blake and Shelley to Chartist newspapers and intellectuals like Carlyle, Marx, Ruskin, and Morris and the social realist novels of American socialist writers like Jack London and Upton Sinclair.

Grieve became a young journalist reporting strikes in the Welsh coalfields in 1911 for Keir Hardie's newspaper, the miners introducing him to American Marxist syndicalist ideas during the heaviest year of strikes Britain had ever seen. Five years later, Quartermaster-Sergeant Grieve of the Royal Army Medical Corps wrote to Ogilvie from Salonica in the middle of the Great War beginning a correspondence—not about the War—but his plans to become a writer, indeed to investigate nothing less than a Scottish Vortex movement, a Modernist Left-led cultural-literary revolution in writing: the Scottish Literary Renaissance (SLR 1920-present).

Five years before MacDiarmid kick-started the SLR from his back-kitchen in 1920s Montrose, he wrote to Ogilvie, fizzing with its ideas—'*I feel like a buried city.*'

My relationship with Hugh MacDiarmid is primarily intertextual, supplemented by other considerations: both of us became Scottish poets and editors, both were Marxists, indeed members of the Communist Party of Great Britain (CPGB 1920-1991), both of us boast Borders ancestry and my father, a local newspaper editor, shared a similar background of ink. We share too, a legacy of auto-didacticism, as most writers do I believe, university educated or not, working class or not, Scottish or not, through the self-directed learning common to becoming and being a writer.

Both traditions, lad o' pairts and autodidactic, met and melded into the ranks of the SLR. In 1911 when Hugh MacDiarmid was covering strikes in the South Wales coalfields, my father was born into a third generation shale mining family in West Lothian. Aged 14 he was offered a scholarship to attend the Royal High School in Edinburgh, which he refused, believing his illegitimacy and miner's background would make life intolerable. He went instead to the pits, learning from the autodidacts already papering the place and whose sayings he quoted for the rest of his days. He taught himself shorthand, became a local journalist after the War and then editor of the local paper by the mid-Sixties. And yes, he read Jack London's *Martin Eden*, a novel about the struggles of a young working-class socialist to become a writer.

My mother was a Borderer who left school aged 13—the only girl in her family—to care for her mother who became crippled with rheumatoid arthritis. She entered 'service' with Edinburgh toffs when she was sixteen, learning to survive on her wits from the older women she worked with—the cook, the lady's maid, the other 'skivvies' amongst whom she classified herself. My mother had her own take on the class war in the Thirties. The lady of the house had a small dog and every day she gave my mother a bar of chocolate for the dog and sixpence for the bus to take it for a walk. She kept the fare, walked the dog, and ate the chocolate.

My mother met my father at a dance in 1938: *'I thought his name was Ralph and he was a grocer, but it was Rab and he was a miner.'* Her parents came to live with them during the War in the same mining rows in which my father had been raised and into which I was born too. When we moved to a council scheme in Bathgate in the early 1950s my parents had a bedroom, my grandparents another, and five sons the other—16 years between the oldest and the youngest.

The Scotland I grew up in from the 1950s to the mid-Sixties comprised a household of six to seven adults all talking and telling stories about working-class life and experience stretching from the late Victorian period to the Vietnam War, a mix of oral testimony and history from below, which I sat and listened to. Culture entered our home via folk memory, the neighbours, pals, the wireless, comics, newspapers, public libraries and the *People's Friend*, my mother's magazine. Culture was largely accessed via picture houses, pubs, dance halls, Burns clubs and football, national and local. Churches, political parties, trade unions, Masonic lodges, Orange lodges, pigeon fanciers and work were likewise key transmission belts for knowledge and moral instruction.

My mother was bewildered by central belt sectarianism: *'I never knew what a Catholic was until I moved to Winchburgh.'* My father's family were staunch Masonic while he opted for the Labour Party, known as the Catholic Labour Party in West Lothian, into the 1970s. He thought Scotland's religiously segregated education embedded sectarianism rather than the reverse and that Glasgow Rangers' policy of not signing Catholics (not abandoned until Graeme Souness signed Mo Johnston in 1989) diminished not only football but Scottish civic and political culture more widely. Three of his five sons married Catholics, none of us religiously minded, like the vast majority of those now living in modern Scotland.

I learned two languages at home and in the street, industrial urban demotic Scots and the Borders tongue of my mother and grandfather (my granny was born in Greenock, the daughter of a shipwright). I learned English by reading her the weekly *Berwickshire News* sent on by my Uncle Bob in the Borders as she lay in her iron cot. I also read her the racing pages of the *Daily Express*, Scotland's largest selling newspaper, for the purpose of placing a one-and—sixpence three cross Irish bet with the scheme's local bookie's runner, five doors along, which invariably included whatever horses Scobie Breasley and Lester Piggott were jockeying that day. I spoke Borders with my grandfather while trailing round the village or scheme or playing draughts or planting vegetables or tying roses up or blethering with my mother or our Borders relatives when we decamped there for the summer.

All this adult orality lay dormant until, aged forty, it began waking me up at 5 or 6 o'clock in the morning, some forgotten word or phrase knocking round my brain, my unconscious summoning my conscious mind, leading to poems like *Game-keepers*:

> My grandfather speaks
> (fed up waiting)
> *Nae gumption! Nae gumption!*
> (here—I—me three an beatin him at draughts)
> I can see the black and green squares
> the dark wood frame
> and him searching for breath
> and soft Borders swears
> Sup yir kail boy! Demned impidence!

My grandparents died in the mid-Sixties around the time that my own George Ogilvie, Douglas Martin, Principal English teacher at Bathgate Academy, hove into view trailing 4th year Higher English. 'Big Ned' was in fact large, six feet four, small blond moustache, military bearing (rumoured a Sergeant-Major in the War), walking stick, indestructible green tweed suit, Aberdeenshire, High Church, lived at the bottom of our scheme with his wife, an ex-nurse, late fifties, no children. He set the topic for the James Simpson Essay Prize, 'Mods and Rockers', which I won, also signing that year for Hibernian FC as a part-time professional footballer.

'Ned' was brilliant on Shakespeare, T.S. Eliot, poetry and criticism, George Orwell, C.P. Snow, Neville Shute and the literary criticism of the 1930s Cambridge Don F.R. Leavis, from which place it was rumoured Ned obtained his First Class Honours Degree. He got his classes to enact sword fights standing on desk lids while he quoted *Macbeth*. He encouraged senior pupils to visit him and his wife at home for tea, buns, and bananas while discussing books and literature and also, in my case, 'communist leanings'. His illegible scrawl on essays contained indiscernible words like 'perfunctory'. In those pre-levelling comprehensive school days, Big Ned was no doubt a lad o' pairts on the look-out for similar spirits, lads and lassies, because that was his teacherly vocation, and I have always in my heart thanked him mightily for it.

I have others to thank likewise from the autodidactic Left whose paths I fell across in my father's local. The Fairway had a lounge intended for the Bathgate bourgeoisie, businessmen and traders, but which also refreshed socialist and social democratic radicals embedded in the education apparatus of late 1960-70s West Lothian and Edinburgh. It was a place Big Ned never entered but would have enjoyed many of its fine arguments on politics, literature and the affairs of the day every Thursday night after college evening classes were over and my father's paper rolling off the presses.

Ned would have spotted his opposite number, Bill Drysdale, Principal Teacher of English at the Lindsay High, the 'non-language' Junior High in Bathgate. Bill had been a communist coal miner in the 1950s who went to Newbattle Adult Education College near Dalkeith, headed by the poet and literary critic Edwin Muir (former friend then enemy of Hugh MacDiarmid) which prepared mainly trade union and labour movement activists with Highers to enter University. There Bill met John Durkin, another Marxist, and they befriended George Mackay Brown, the Orcadian writer, as brilliantly described in Maggie Fergusson's biography, for which both supplied vital details.

These men were in their fifties as was Harry Ferry, an economic history lecturer, then Head of West Lothian Further Education College in Bathgate, plus Donald McArthur from Lewis, a former merchant navy seaman, who worked as an English lecturer for Harry and likewise was a late entrant to university education. Present too was my older brother Alan, another mature student who obtained a politics and economics degree at Strathclyde, studying with the Marxist labour historian, John Foster, before returning to work for Harry at the college until the 1990s. To this kernel was added my father, a Harold Wilson socialist like Harry, whereas Donald was more Bennite with Bill, John, and Alan, all communist-socialist Marxists. During bouts and in from the adjoining bar would float Eric the Red, Eric Atkinson, communist party organiser for West Lothian and a full-time agitator. Let battle commence! I watched and listened and sipped my shandy.

I forget the arguments, which have since been overtaken by a totally different anti-neoliberal discourse and moral universe. Bill Drysdale still sticks though, reciting Shelley in the middle of the hubble and speaking of his dead father and how he had walked up the Bathgate Hills, not a religious person, and thinking that so long as his brother and himself were alive, so too would be his father. Jon Dirkin spoke of the sans-culottes, ragged arsed losers of the French Revolution. My father sang Burns. Eric lamented the Troubles in Ireland. Whenever I read of MacDiarmid and his cronies Norman MacCaig, Sydney Goodsir Smith and Hamish Henderson stravaiging the bars of 1950s Edinburgh or tearing lumps out of each other in the 1960s *flyting* in *The Scotsman* over the merits of art poetry versus folksong, I think of them. (What MacDiarmid had feared most, of course, was that folk might lead a return to the kailyard culture he had created the SLR to obliterate).

Another memory, 1971, and I'm returning to Armadale from Glasgow on a double-decker bus, a student worker on placement. The stop before mine, a middle-aged man wearing a belted blue gabardine raincoat and bunnet and carrying a small leather briefcase, taps me on the shoulder, no one else around—*'It's good tae see a young fella reading a book like that, son. Ye'll no go far wrang,'* he said, then disappeared down the stairs. It was Robert Tressell's socialist novel *The Ragged Trousered Philanthropists* (1911).

They are all dead now, the earlier named, except for John Foster, International Secretary of the Communist Party, and my brother Alan, now joined the Greens, called the gardening section of the SNP rather unkindly by George Galloway, the SNP now unlikely to attract MacDiarmid to its petty-bourgeois banner. I wrote a poem celebrating the 60th anniversary of the October Revolution in 1977 called *The Russian Revolution in Bathgate* that refers to John Foster and Eric Atkinson. Eric was the Scottish Treasurer of the CPGB until its demise in 1991. His father had been an election agent for Manny Shinwell in the 1920s. It was not unusual to get a phone call from Eric beginning—*'Just been reading Gorky, comrade, great stuff.'* Eric's bookshelves contained stuff the Bathgate Library staff had never heard of and would not have stocked, anyway.

If dialectical materialism had ever become an Olympic event, Eric would have won gold for Scotland. A master glazier repeatedly interrupted by blacklisting, when Eric spoke local events rubbed shoulders with global affairs as the Party's principled position was defended against a tidal wave of daily distortions, depredations and downright lies peddled by every news agency in the land, from the benign (BBC) to the malign (*Catholic Herald*) with the single shining exception of the *Daily Worker* and its love-child, the *Morning Star*. Eric and his unswerving wife, Marjorie, were from that generation of communists who supported the Soviet Union because they saw it being attacked by the same people who were attacking them and their class.

Eric's communism, unlike MacDiarmid's, was not sectarian but Broad Left. He was friends with the Catholic priest in Bathgate for years, who occasionally asked him to fix the chapel's stained-glass windows for free, and Eric, master glazier, always obliged. He would gleefully recount how on one such occasion when he was passing a local pub there stood an old crony, a large Blue-Nose, who asked where he was heading with his bag. When Eric said he was on his way down to the chapel '*to put some windows in,*' the worthy said, '*haud oan a minute, Eric, I'll gie ye a hand.*'

Little did I suspect then that I would join the CPGB myself years later in Edinburgh, provoked by Mrs Thatcher's Falklands War rather than worn down by Eric's fabled persistence. Nor that when the party dissolved itself in 1991, I would begin writing poetry. Nor that my first published poem *Brithers* would appear in a Scots literary magazine bearing the title of MacDiarmid's long poem *Cencrastus*. Nor that in doing so I would in effect become part of the 3rd-4th generation of the SLR. *Brithers* in fact mentions MacDiarmid in its central passage, linking my father and all the other shared identities and diverse influences in the buried city I seem to have spent much of my life trying to unearth and which, unaccountably, I still am:

> We create oorsels as he did, and MacDiarmid,
> wi words and terrible talk and a' the slavers
> o' the Scottish workin-class, an aristocracy o' havers
> pissin wi' the poor against the same bloody wa'.'

Gerard Cairns

was born and brought up in Easterhouse and has lived in the East End of Glasgow all his life. He has been active in republican and socialist politics since he was 17. He was the organiser of Springburn Branch of the Scottish Socialist Party in the late 1990s and early 2000s and Secretary of the John MacLean Society for a longer period. He has supported the cause of an independent, socialist Scotland since his teenage years. In recent years political activism has given way to writing and learning the Gaelic language. Gerry is the author of The Red and the Green—A Portrait of John MacLean. His most recent book *No Language, No Nation! The Life of the Honourable Ruaraidh Erskine of Marr*, was published earlier this year by Rymour Books.

The John Maclean Society: A Brief Memoir

Can you imagine this scene? A good many years after you leave this earth, there is a gathering to remember your contribution whatever that may be. There is a close family relative, the leader of a religious beatnik community, the person who you felt had betrayed you, and the country's leading, legendary poet all speaking in your honour. It may be beyond our comprehension. This is exactly what happened with the famous Red Clydesider, John Maclean (1879-1923).

In Glasgow's Grand Hotel at Central Station, the John Maclean Society was officially inaugurated on Sunday 31 March 1968, almost 45 years after his death from pneumonia and the effects of state victimisation. This was not the first time that he had been remembered. Tom Anderson had organised annual John Maclean marches from Eastwood Toll to his gravesite for years after his death until the late 1940s. Also, famously, he was remembered at a meeting of the Scotland-USSR Friendship Society in 1948 by the singing of a new song by Hamish Henderson. William Noble gave the first rendition of *The John Maclean March*. Twenty years later, his two daughters, Jean and Nan, were among the sponsors who included prominent Labour, Communist, and Nationalist leaders, poets and contemporaries such as Manny Shinwell and Harry McShane, the latter having left Maclean's Tramp Trust Unlimited to join the Communist Party in 1922. Maclean never forgave him.

It is to the credit of Nan Milton Maclean, the youngest daughter and driving force of the Society, that she did. You could call it emotional intelligence. McShane went on to be a massive supporter of the Society and he spoke on that afternoon along with the Rev. Lord MacLeod of Fuinary who—as George MacLeod—had set up the Iona Community, Hugh MacDiarmid, Nan, George Leslie of the SNP, and there was also a *dramatic presentation* organised by the folk singer/songwriter, Morris Blythman. It was a formidable line-up. The meeting also agreed on a constitution and endorsed the following aims:

> To commemorate the dedicated life of John Maclean and his outstanding and sacrificial efforts to emancipate the working class of Scotland and the world; and to do so by encouraging and assisting research into the works and life of John Maclean, including his writings, lectures, speeches, and related matters, and apply them to the circumstances of today.

This author was not in attendance for the very good reason that I was not born until February 1969 although at a later date I did get to meet some of those who were there that day.

The main observation that should be made is that any organisation should be judged by aims and objectives and how successfully it met those. By this measurement, the Society was an unqualified success. In terms of publications, the Society reprinted many of Maclean's pamphlets including *The Irish Tragedy: Scotland's Disgrace, A Plea for Working Class Education in Scotland, The War after the War* among others, and also salvaged his Scottish Labour College lecture notes on economics (which had been thankfully kept by his friend James Clunie). Clunie was still around to be one of the Society's sponsors. As we shall see, the Society became a forum for fine lectures, good debate, radical poetry, and folk song.

1973 would be a big year for the Society and for Maclean's memory. Two main biographies, eponymously titled, appeared on bookshelves, written by Nan and John Broom, respectively. Broom was an Orcadian and another original sponsor. Both were distinctive, objective and highly readable. The Society also made a fine contribution in print. *Homage to John Maclean* was a collection of poems and songs edited by T.S. Law and Thurso Berwick (Blythman's pen name). It is a much under-rated work that has long since been out of print. For good or ill, the poets grasped the memory of MacLean and made it their own. The famous poetic license ran riot, producing controversy, passion, hagiography and a legend that is still associated with Maclean's name today. All three of Scotland's languages were represented, but it was fitting that the first and last contributions were in Gaelic from the pens of Sorley Maclean and Derrick Thomson no less. Maclean, whose father was from the clan's own island of Mull, had written under the pseudonym Gael, in the early part of the century.

The Society was instrumental in raising public finance that year for a cairn to be erected near his home in Pollockshaws with an inscription that described him as the *'Scottish link in the golden chain of world socialism'*. The late Sean Connery also subscribed, fresh from his documentary that he produced on the Upper Clyde Shipbuilders in 1971. Many of the same faces were in Pollockshaws for its unveiling as there had been in the Grand Hotel five years earlier.

Activity continued throughout the seventies and eighties, staying true to the aim agreed in 1968. Monthly meetings, folk nights and annual memorial lectures gave the feel of something vibrant. I have in front of me a newsletter from August 1984 issued by Nan. The feature for that year was 'The Way Forward for Scottish Socialists.' There was a lengthy feature on the Campaign for a Scottish Assembly with the link made between the CSA's call for Scottish MPs to form an Interim Assembly in Edinburgh to Maclean's own call in his last election address for the Labour MPs to return to Scotland and abstain just as the Irish had done in 1918. A look at the line-up of musicians and singers shows the drawing power of the Society. A folk night in honour of Morris Blythman attracted Stramash, Hamish Henderson, Sue Robertson, the Clutha, Jim Brown, Arthur Johnstone, and Maggie Faulds. Nan would have been 71 and was stepping down as Secretary but stayed on as Treasurer.

Future Secretaries would include Ellen Mitchell, a young Kenny MacAskill, and a young me!

*

I joined the Society in 1988. There was no Secretary at that point. The Chairman was the historian Jim Young, who made a fine contribution to Scottish working-class history. I suppose I became Secretary by default. Things weren't the same. Hindsight tells me that the vibrancy was not there, but that did not stop us because it did not feel that way at the time. We still had fine speakers, music and some fine poetry, especially from the Galloway based John Manson. He would make the trek up for many meetings in Glasgow and we also had the inimitable Glasgow Irishman, Freddy Anderson. Sometimes the music was impromptu.

Someone would bring a guitar to the meeting. These meetings were still monthly but had moved from the Star Club in Carlton Place over the Rio Clyde to the City Halls. Our members were just getting older, and they were mostly male. Very few female comrades attended. Audrey Canning, from the Willie Gallacher Memorial Library, was a solid supporter of the Society. Between 1990 and 1992, the Society had a programme of lectures on themes of Marxism, Anarchism and the Scottish National Question with speakers including the academic Hillel Ticktin, Bill Johnston, the idiosyncratic Marxist, Paul Smith, and the anarchist, Farquhar McLay. These lectures were published in the Society's last published book, Unmasking Reality. Bill was one of the original sponsors, a veteran trade unionist, a member of the International Workers of the World (nicknamed the Wobblies) and former SNP Lord Provost of Clydebank. He would be Chairman of the Society for a spell in the nineties.

The Society would remain a treasure trove of socialist history and was graced by excellent lectures from fine historians such as Jim Young, John Ford and Stephen Coyle. John was the Society's Treasurer and had the best beard ever, even better than Karl Marx's, and there was the odd occasion when I heard whisper that he looked like Rasputin! It was an excellent political education. We also had our own dominies in the form of Donald Anderson, the republican socialist chief of the clan, no less, who tried bravely to reclaim his ancestral land in Kenneddar, Moray, from the RAF; and Allan Armstrong who has published some fine work on Scottish history and James Connolly's Edinburgh connections.

Nan Milton died in 1991. I had the pleasure of meeting her on a couple of occasions, and she was truly inspiring. She always kept abreast of Society activities. The John Maclean March was resurrected and throughout the nineties, Glasgow's Lord Provost, invariably then a Labour Party member, would speak at the graveside. The Society cultivated this relationship as Maclean's memory always played on their cold socialist consciences. This got us funding to reprint Nan's biography, a face-lift for the cairn in Pollockshaws and a replacement for the plaque outside the City Halls which mysteriously went missing.

Attendances at meetings dwindled throughout the nineties. In early 1998, I received a telephone call from a producer called Doreen McArdle. She was truly one of Maclean's *'freens in Springburn'*, where she lived. She had an idea to produce a 'Great John Maclean Night' to commemorate the 75th anniversary of his death. I was heavily involved in the organisation, but all praise to Doreen. The 'Night' went ahead in Glasgow's Arches Theatre on Sunday 29 November. The late writer and artist, Alasdair Gray, designed the leaflet. There was music from the Song Factory and the McCluskey Brothers as well as the St. Francis pipe band. There were speeches and readings. The highlight, unforgettable to my memory, was the guest of honour—Hamish Henderson, who stood up, arms in the air, giving it laldy to his own *John Maclean March*. That was 50 years after William Noble had introduced the song. MacLean had *come hame tae the Clyde* and it was the last hurrah for the Society.

Almost... we did continue into the new millennium, meeting more intermittently. The last hurrah did come in the Scotia Bar in Glasgow filming for the BBC programme *Power to the People*. All the old faces that we could call were told to turn up and be on the telly! The format was a 'meeting' of the Society, and the folk singer, Ian Davison, sung his own song in tribute to Maclean. The Secretary got back to his computer to take issue with some allegations on MacLean's mental instability in the programme. We have always rejected such notions and always will.

The Society never formally folded. It has gone into abeyance as most of our members just died. Maclean's memory—thankfully—hasn't. Two new biographies came out over 2017 and 2018 and the last author, Henry Bell, has taken Maclean into blogs and to the Radical Independence Convention. There is still a place for a teacher of the working class to expose the injustice of the system we live under. There is still a place for genuine internationalism and human sister/brotherhood to denounce war and conquest. As Scotland moves towards independence, John Maclean reminds us that we can seize it as an opportunity to change our country for the better or let those same exploiters snuggle under their covers, safe in the knowledge that more of the same is on the way.

Nan Milton was the first Secretary. I was the last. That may be nice for my ego, but hopefully someone else will come along. There is still work to do. I was still a teenager when Pat Lally, the Glasgow Provost, suggested that there should be a statue built to Maclean. I was at a meeting in the McLellan Galleries sometime in the late 1980s and a very frail Nan made a contribution from the floor to much applause. The best monument to her father's memory, she suggested, was not a statue. It was a resurrected Scottish Labour College, training and educating the working class. This will give us new teachers and a modern curriculum with much to learn. They are fitting last words from a member of the clan Maclean.

Donald Smith

was born in Glasgow of Irish parents. He is a storyteller, author and educationalist. As Director of the Netherbow Arts Centre from 1982, and founding Director of the Scottish Storytelling Centre from 2003 to 2014, Donald has been in the thick of cultural and social developments in Scotland, and beyond, over three decades. He believes in the power of culture to enhance confidence and well-being, and in the vital importance of individuals and communities being the inheritors and makers of their own stories. He has also been the Director of the International Storytelling Festival since its inception in 1989, and a founding member of Traditional Arts and Culture Scotland since 2014. He has written plays and novels, as well as producing, adapting or directing over eighty plays, and he has published a series of books about Scotland.

Seeing the Voice: A Memoir of Hamish Henderson

In 1979 I had three memorable encounters with Hamish Henderson. I can see now that his influence was then growing, but to begin with I had no idea who he was or what he stood for. These encounters were public occasions, and nothing in this Memoir is based on insider knowledge, yet I intend to look beyond standard accounts.

It was April 1979. The Devolution referendum was underway and the first Edinburgh International Folk Festival, directed by John Barrow, had started. I was in a first postgraduate year at Edinburgh University's Divinity Faculty; my wife Alison was at Moray House College of Education. My training as a Church of Scotland minister was not going well for me, or in fairness, for them; and I was moving to the School of Scottish Studies.

We had to choose between going to the festival or doing a weekly shop. Having opted out of the food, we were rewarded by unexpected snow that left cancelled university conferences and an abundance of salvageable supplies. We booked into the Folk Festival conference 'The People's Past.' Hamish Henderson was the prevailing spirit, a notable contributor on ballads, and commentator on most aspects of the day, including an extra loo break to cope with liquid lunch. But the overall impact was a systematic challenge to accepted conventions of history writing, at a time when Scotland's past was being re-examined. This was Hamish Henderson as radical educator and collaborator, putting folk memory and its bearers at the forefront. Inevitably we followed on the next week to a talk Hamish gave at Riddle's Court, HQ of the Workers Educational Association.

I cannot remember the ostensible subject, but there was a lot about Calvinism. Hamish expounded that, whatever the historical twists and turns, Calvinism was a repressive ideology in Scottish culture, psychology and society; but folk tradition showed that the majority of Scots had never

Hamish Henderson by Bob Starrett

been fully signed up. Henderson became focused on a religious metaphor of *'divesting—in the vestry'*: we had to divest ourselves of layers of preconceptions and misconceptions before we could come to grips with Scotland and her people. There was an unexpected touch of ritual in the whole presentation.

On this occasion, I sensed levels of complexity in Hamish Henderson. How many layers were still undivested?

> Change elegy into hymn—remake it—
> Don't fail again. Like the potent
> Sap in the branches, once bare, and now brimming
> With routh of green leavery,
> Remake it, and renew.

('Under the Earth I Go')

In October 1979, Odysseus Elytis was awarded the Nobel Prize for Literature, and the Greek society organised a celebration. I went along to find that Hamish was *'fear an taighe'*. Though he was his normal cardiganed, bespectacled, grey-haired, eagle-eyed self, Hamish hosted with mantic, bacchic exuberance, channelling a stream of Greek, English, Italian, Scots, Gaelic and some Latin for good measure. It was a revelation of living culture, beyond the books, and of a joy that was political (Elytis versus the Greek colonels), personal and psychic. Bardic voices were at play, yet embodied in the communal experience: we had seen the voice, and for a time became the voice.

What empowered that eloquence and influence, in the year of '79? I would like to acknowledge three broad areas—the folklore collecting, the cultural politics, and the making of poems and songs.

Hamish Henderson's contribution to folklore in Scotland was part of a wider movement in which Calum MacLean was another key influence. Hamish's influence was wide because he linked the sources to contemporary culture and politics; but his biggest contribution is the close relationship he formed with Scotland's Travellers.

This theme is richly demonstrated by Tim Neat in books and films; I want only to underline that Hamish received as much as he gave in this mutual bonding. I understand that, because over decades of my own storytelling, I have benefitted hugely from the friendship of Willie McPhee, Sheila Stewart, Duncan Williamson, Stanley Robertson and Jess Smith, amongst others. Yet it went deeper for Hamish since, as an illegitimate child and orphan, he felt himself to be 'outcast' from his own roots, and in the Traveller community he found a substitute family. And this at a crucial time, when after the trauma and strange fellowship of war, Hamish was in need of acceptance and healing. Sheila Stewart characteristically hits the nail on its head with this to Tim Neat:

> Hamish told us about the homes he was in. He had a hard life but he said it wisnae hard like the Travellers had living in tents wi every hand against them. He had the grieving for his mother but we had the Tinker's Curse. It was Hamish who drew us back to the fire.

(Poetry Becomes People, Vol 2 p. 49)

We shall return to Henderson's family, but these words tell us a lot about vulnerability and about Hamish's layers. They are also testimony to the life wisdom that many Traveller tradition bearers possess, and have generously shared with outsiders.

What of the politics? Hamish Henderson was a democratic socialist, a humanist, a cultural nationalist, and an internationalist. And before the name 'Antonio Gramsci' is uttered, it is useful to see Henderson in a line from Keir Hardie and Robert Cunninghame Graham, John Maclean and James Maxton. It was MacLean that Hamish channelled into his radical song-making, as he was to channel Nelson Mandela in a later but related struggle.

Gramsci figures when you consider the role of culture in the socialist and communist cause, since he was the first major thinker of the left to discuss popular culture. Hamish encountered Gramsci's influence during his war service in Italy and made the first translation into English of the Italian radical's *Prison Letters*. There was a connection also between Gramsci's Sardinian background within Italy, and Henderson's Scottish identity within Britain. Yet, as a more recent researcher, Corey Gibson points out, Hamish made little of Gramsci's more technical concepts such as 'cultural hegemony'.

So, in 2017, on an epic train journey across Europe, I sat down to re-read the *Prison Letters*. I was en route via Weimar to Rudolstadt in Thuringia for the *Weltmusik* Festival, where I was rewarded by joining in a bilingual Scots-German version of Henderson's 'Freedom Come All Ye' led by Steve Byrne, under the sign of the EU Saltire.

There is relatively little in Gramsci's prison letters or papers about folklore. He is focused on Italian society and interrogating why the nineteenth century *Risorgimento* ended up with fascism. Gramsci's twofold explanation focuses on the conservatism of the dominant Roman Catholic Church, and the failure of middle-class intellectuals to identify with the lived realities of the majority population. Instead, they had focused on their own values, culture and status.

Hamish Henderson undoubtedly applied that analysis to Scottish society, past and present, though in this case the dominant religious influence was Calvinism, merging by mid-twentieth century into an economically driven managerialism. What one might call a secular, materialist Calvinism controlled society by repressing cultural and psychological initiative, while protecting the vested interests of middle class, professional Scotland.

In Henderson's sights were the ministers, academics, politicians, lawyers, journalists, writers, broadcasters, and teachers who had signed up to the prevailing values of the British state which in return gave them economic security and social privilege. Everything in Hamish's writing, teaching, creative work, campaigning, and behaviour exuded a more attractive dissenting alternative. His folk culture, with its vision of *commonweal*, directly threatened all forms of the Scottish establishment, and that is why Hamish was so loathed and feared on a personal level. By being himself, he threatened the many false selves of Scottish self-justification and class division. In this regard, Henderson understood and challenged cultural hegemony, moral presumption, unaccountable exercise of power, and failure of common vision. That battle continues because middle-class privilege, normally disguised as economic rationalism, remains a principal block to progress of all kinds in Scotland. Judging by the work of Dario Fo and Franca Rame, the same is true of Italy, though there, as in England, right-wing populism is also in the frame.

Hamish Henderson's performance art draws on centuries of Scottish and European tradition—Celtic design, the medieval makars, oral crafting, musical memory—as well as individual talent. Alongside a few defining essays and letters, Henderson's songs and poems are his most vital legacy, and the easiest way in which to access that legacy, as he himself hoped.

The *kist o treasurs* becomes richer as you move from the *Collected Poems and Songs* (2000) painstakingly honed by Raymond Ross in collaboration with Hamish, to the comprehensive abundance of the 2019 *Collected Poems* edited by Corey Gibson. Go direct to these sources, and let them sing and speak, as to quote Hamish in his sixth wartime Elegy '*my words would be pointless.*'

> So the words that I have looked for, and must go on looking for,
> are words of whole love, which can slowly gain the power to
> reconcile and heal.

(*Elegies for the Dead of Cyreniaca*)

In Hamish's hands, art transforms into life and love, which in turn transfigures into art. There is a hint of Patrick Geddes (another Perthshire offspring) in all this—life is the green leaf, and art the flower. But does that divest all the Hamish Henderson layers? In reality, they have become deeper and more intertwined.

In his monumental biography, Tim Neat gives two accounts of Hamish's Perthshire parentage and family. In the main text he gives what we might call the preferred, or in some respects, 'official account' that Hamish's father was a little-known former soldier named Scott, who took some responsibility for Janet Henderson's illegitimate son. In an Appendix, however, Tim Neat also gives a sympathetic account of the alternative version that Hamish Henderson's father was John Stewart-Murray, 8th Duke of Atholl, usually known as Bardie. Now that the commemoration of Hamish's centenary of 2019 is over, I would like to choose more clearly between these two versions.

There is a strong circumstantial context for a love affair between Janet Henderson, the attractive Perthshire Queen's Nurse, returned from service in France, working in the hospital that Blair Castle had become, on the one side; and the new Duke of Atholl, recently returned from the nightmare dysentery-ridden hellhole of Gallipoli that effectively finished his prize military career, on the other. This was a *flyting* of Life versus Death. Then add to the mix local knowledge of Bardie's affairs, with other possible births, and the Duchess of Atholl's summary of her marriage as a 'working partnership'. Further, as Angus Calder often remarked, how else can you explain the well-concealed financial support given to Hamish Henderson's education in England, before and after his mother's untimely death?

But there is another less noticed context—the cultural passions of the Atholl Stewart-Murrays. The 7th Duke (Hamish's grandfather?) championed Gaelic culture and insisted, within months of his succession, on legally restoring the Stewart name to his Murray inheritance. He then devoted much of his life to documenting this Scottish heritage. The Duke's two daughters, Evelyn and Dorothea, inherited his passion. They became noted collectors of, respectively, Scottish folk narrative and folksong.

But it was Bardie, on succeeding his father as the 8th Duke of Atholl, who was to initiate and drive the biggest cultural, social and religious project in post-WW1 Scotland—the Scottish National War Memorial—which came to signify and express the traumatised grief of a nation.

Whitehall had decreed and funded one national war memorial—the Imperial War Museum in London. Bardie lobbied furiously for a Scottish national war memorial, which was reluctantly conceded on condition that he could raise the money. He proceeded over a decade not only to raise the finance but to brood over every aspect of the design (at Edinburgh Castle), the contents, the artworks, and the public engagement, including a Roll of Honour that aimed to record every man and woman belonging in some way to Scotland who had served. In addition, the commissioned artworks embodied the men and women (Queen's Nurses, for example) and even animals who had been part of the sacrificial effort. This was no common memorial, as Duncan Macmillan has persuasively shown, but a stunning tribute in stone, glass, poetry and paint.

When the Scottish National War Memorial opened in 1927, it exceeded all expectations, becoming the inclusive national shrine for a people's grief. It is hard not to draw a direct line from this endeavour to Hamish Henderson's mission, in the wake of a second traumatic World War, to gather up the culture of a people and nation, in an inclusive act of remembrance and healing, and a pledge for change. In addition, this followed hard, personal experience of military service—like father, like son.

Consider the familiar BBC footage of Hamish leaning out of a back window at the School of Scottish Studies in George Square to watch, benignly yet distantly, the Royal Company of Archers on the Meadows. This was a world to which he might have belonged, but from which he and his mother were exiled, and which he chose in the interests of his own vocation not to acknowledge. Until that is in the final years of his life.

Raymond Ross's obituary in *The Scotsman* attracted attention because of its comment on Hamish Henderson's sexuality, but the more newsworthy element was Hamish's admission that his father was 'a cousin to the Dukes of Atholl'. This statement was made to Raymond Ross, and noted at a time when they were working together on the *Collected Poems and Songs*; Hamish was well aware that Raymond (editor, reviewer, journalist) was a likely obituarist.

It is not however a straightforward statement, and has sometimes been discounted because there is no obvious candidate for such 'a cousin'. What though if Hamish's words (obituary brief) are deliberately ambivalent? At the time of speaking, Hamish's late father had been since 1957 a cousin to the Dukes of Atholl. That is because the direct Stewart-Murray line expired when Bardie and his four siblings all died against the odds 'without (legitimate) issue'. So in this late, defining remark, Hamish acknowledged a heritage that meant a lot to him, while still protecting his anonymity, and the power of his life's work to identify with everyman and everywoman. There is added poignancy if he was in effect 'last of the line'—an unrecognised Prince, not over the water but in his own land.

Some may be uncomfortable with these cultural genetics, yet recognise that a hidden vulnerability underlay Hamish's uncanny gift of affecting human hearts and souls. And he knew it.

Under the earth I go
On the oak leaf I stand
I ride on a filly that never was foaled
And I carry the dead in my hand.
There's method in my magic!

('Under the Earth I Go')

I for one am profoundly grateful to have heard the voice, and seen the seer. But the heritage of Hamish Henderson is given without qualification to all those in love with freedom.

Honor Pringle

was a post-war child and her first home, due to a chronic housing shortage, was a Nissen hut called Lochinvar in Leith. The hut was one room, with kitchen and toilet facilities in a separate building. Her family then moved to Redhall, an Edinburgh housing scheme built after the war. On leaving school she attended Skerry's College and then worked for many years in a high street bank. With the financial crash of 2008 she began working part-time in Waitrose for a further ten years and finally retired at the age of 71.

Willie Cock-Eyes, the Communist Dues Collector

I remember an incident from my younger days when I lived in Redhall. There was a knock on the door and I went to open it. Standing there was the local Communist Party collector of monthly dues. Both my parents were members of the Party.

Willie was a kind, gentle man and quite shy too. Unfortunately, he suffered from *strabismus*—a condition where the person's eyes are squint or crossed, commonly known in those days as cock-eyed. It was difficult to tell who or what he was actually looking at. I never knew his surname, and he was known in our house simply as Willie Cock-Eyes.

On hearing the knock on the door my mother shouted down the stairs, 'Who is it, Honor?'

'It's Willie Cock-Eyes, mum,' I immediately blurted out.

I drew breath in shock at myself, filled with a mortifying sense of embarrassment. Willie, for his part, offered me a quiet half smile as if to ease my sense of shame. My mum had now come downstairs, and she invited Willie into our living room. She gave me in passing one of her withering stares as if to say *'that was awful'* which it undoubtedly was.

I have often thought of Willie and of my parents all being communists. As I look back and look also at today's world, I think that the idea of communism remains the best idea that humanity ever created. Yes, it was practised in too authoritarian a way, but the idea of a classless society where everyone has a fair chance in life remains the greatest ideal of history.

Mairi Murphy

worked as an auxiliary in her first job after leaving school, then moved into radiography. She believes in the health service and in free geriatric care. She is proud of her working-class roots and her family's shipbuilding and railway past. She graduated from Glasgow University's MLitt with distinction where she was awarded the 2016 Alistair Buchan Prize for poetry. She has been published in *New Writing Scotland*, poetry magazines and online, and her first collection, *Observance*, was published by Clothoderick Press in 2018. Providing workshops for the inaugural Paisley Book Festival, this year her poetry was featured online for Paisley's 'Sma' Shot' Festival. She is the co-founder of Four-em Press and editor of *Glasgow Women Poets*.

Shift

My mum said I would never take wearing a white coat for granted after I'd worn a grey auxiliary's uniform. I'd not to think of myself as better than anyone else and this was the way to learn. She wore a yellow dress in the hospital canteen and it was hard enough—no one noticed her face. It turned out I could stand for an hour in X-Ray with a patient and no one spoke to me—till, as a student in my white dress, it was as if I had materialised. Lesson learned —always treat people the same.

Everyone seemed to be the same. Except people in 'bought houses'. They seemed to be a different class. Even so, doctors and lawyers sent their daughters to my school—the curriculum offered Greek, Latin, Russian, or German; the nuns expected us to go to university. We were the last year of an all-girls before the school became a mixed comprehensive.

My dad had sent me for a job in the geriatric hospital halfway through sixth year. No point in staying on if I was accepted for radiography. The Nursing Officer who interviewed me didn't ask me, like the other girls, if I was on the pill—instead, he told me what type I was, 'convent educated—never made a bed'. I was the last intake of auxiliary staff in January 1979, before Mrs Thatcher's election in May.

Sisters ruled, and their word was law. Patients at the top of the list. Scrub lockers. Make beds sharp with hospital corners. Seams of pillow cases face away from the door of the ward. Bed bath with tenderness. Never take a patient on a trolley through a door feet first. Pin your cap on tight with crossed kirbies. Always wear your cape outside. Black polished shoes. Do your best. Plenty of staff—enough to put on music and have a ceilidh in the afternoon, enough to have a sing-song in the ward. Never say we are in Craw Road; this is not the poorhouse. Enough staff to care. A job in a hospital was a job for life—families employed, generations—in stores, laundries, autoclaves, all on site. Forums and discussion groups, pantomimes, shows.

A nursing school. Life.

I missed voting in the election by four days. When staff left, they were no longer replaced. Time and motion men followed the porters about to shave off any surplus. No student help for the wards in summer. More management. More accountants. Less money. More uncertainty. Centralisation. Outsourcing.

It's hard to be the last 18-year-old who knew life before Mrs Thatcher —but it's even more important to document. Our past may be our future, we have to remember. No matter what colour your coat.

Sophie Parke

was born in Glasgow but raised in Auckland, New Zealand until she was thirteen, when she returned to Scotland. She is currently in her second year at the University of Oxford where she studies English Literature. She has had her work published in *The Isis Magazine, Texture Magazine* and *The Cherwell Magazine*. She is a staff writer for *Texture Magazine*, creative director of *That Hot Zine*, and host of KB'd on Subcity Radio Station. The following article was published in *The Isis Magazine HT21*.

A Love Letter to the Glaswegian Dialect

'DJ Fucking Badboy here
Steamin as Shite
Am 'boot ti tell you a story
'Boot ma Friday nite...'

This is how DJ Badboy's 'Friday Nite' opens—a track well familiar to anyone who spent their teens at sweaty Glaswegian house parties. I once made the error of writing about 'Friday Nite' for one of my university essays, resulting in a tutorial where my highly respected Oxford Professor asked me with deadpan sincerity to explain what it means to be 'steamin as shite'. How was I supposed to convey the sheer *culture* imbued within these lines to anyone who hadn't grown up in Glasgow? That these lines were as well-worn into the psyche of the modern Glaswegian teenager as the works of Shakespeare: to be, or not to be steamin as shite, that is the question... After I gave an abridged explanation ('It means getting wankered, Professor'), it left me thinking: how do you explain the love affair Glaswegians have with their own dialect?

After all, it's a dialect near unintelligible to the outsider. Urban Glasgow English (GE), characterised by a thick regional accent spoken at rapid pace, is primarily composed of slang and dialectic phrases, and is densely expletive. Particularly fond of expletive infixation, Glaswegians effortlessly cleave their lexis to insert 'fuck' at every opportunity, creating words like 'de-fuckin-stress,' 'abso-fuckin-lutely' or ''fan-fuckin-tastic'. Yet, for all its incomprehensibility, GE is beloved by those who use it. There are entire books written in GE, and a Glaswegian section of Twitter where tweets are written using spelling that mirrors regional pronunciation, such as 'ahm,' 'baws' and 'shite'. A brief foray into Glaswegian Tinder confirmed that there's Tinder in GE as well, with a few particularly memorable bios including the lyrical: 'Am the specky fucker, no looking for a relationship the now, just want ma hole' and 'Who's wantin pumped?'

In fact, much of the appeal of GE for Glaswegians is precisely *just how* difficult it is to understand. GE acts as a linguistic tariff on Glaswegian identity since only the privileged few who can comprehend it are able to fully participate in the inner workings of Glaswegian culture. As someone who grew up abroad but went to high school in Glasgow, I've experienced being both a linguistic outsider and insider. At first, GE appears to be an entirely new language rather than a dialect, with translations required for everyday objects such as a stairwell (a 'close'), groceries ('messages'), graffiti ('menties') and tobacco ('snout'). Some pieces of vernacular even have long lists of alternative translations, as I soon discovered when trying to learn the many different words that Glaswegians have for getting drunk, also known as, 'gettin mad wi it', 'muntered', 'reekin', 'rubbered', 'blootered', 'pished', 'goosed', 'oot yer tree', 'steaming', and 'ratarsed'... an impressive linguistic plethora which shines a spotlight on what Glaswegians are most passionate about. Or, as my weary dad who works in Glasgow's A&E Department would drily add, one could say the same for the multiple words meaning 'stab'.

However, once you familiarise yourself with the dialect, the door to Glaswegian culture swings wide open. You enter a world of extremes, where everything is 'top class' or 'fucking pish', and everyone is either 'absolutely buzzing' or 'totally raging'. You break situations down to their bare essentials ('Covid? Shitemare'). After memorising key chants such as 'here we, here we, here we fuckin go', you learn that a concert can never truly begin until thousands of you have yelled it till your voices are hoarse. You recognise cultural movements such as 'Taps Aff' where one removes one's shirt 'most often in the event of warm weather' but occasionally for reasons of 'simple antagonism' (as defined by Urban Dictionary). You learn about important anthropological phenomena unique to Glasgow, such as the attribution of 'specky' to an individual—one of the last places in the world where it's still considered a legitimate insult. What is more fascinating is that you don't even have to wear glasses to be considered 'specky', as it has more to do with having a 'Specky Aura' than whether you are visually impaired or not.

All jokes aside, the maintenance of GE forms an important resistance against Standard English (SE). If Glaswegians were to wake up tomorrow and begin speaking SE, we would lose so much of the culture, history, and humour that identifies Glasgow. Hang onto your local slang—it holds the key to your city. I've come to realise this more and more during my time at Oxford, a university renowned for its wanky old-school propriety. In protest, I find myself using more Glaswegian dialect at Oxford than I used when I actually lived in Glasgow. Full to the brim with hometown pride, it brings me great pleasure to holler down the corridors: 'Let's get steamin the night!' —albeit in a slightly Kiwi accent.

This is my love letter to the Glaswegian dialect: I love you, and when I am away, I miss your constant effing and blinding, your directness and your enthusiasm. I hope that it won't be too long until I'm back in a grotty nightclub with my pals and hear a familiar distant rumble... it will start quietly, and then it will grow louder, and louder, until it's unmistakeable ... Here we... Here we... Here we fucking go...

Coinneach Maciver

grew up in a crofting family on the Isle of Lewis. He taught Physics at secondary schools in Edinburgh where he was also the EIS rep. He is a former member of the Labour Party and was active in the campaign against South-African apartheid. Though now retired from teaching, he can still do a day's labouring with his son-in-law who is a builder.

Mary and Christina Ann

In the summer of 1912, two girls were born in the small village of Tong on the Isle of Lewis. They were born into large families—each girl the youngest of eight children. The village was very poor by the standards of these times. Fifty years earlier a visiting government official commenting on conditions in the village reported that he had never seen such destitution—not even in the poorest parts of Donegal. Fishing was the main source of income, and the crofting lands were not very fertile.

The two girls became friends and sat together in school for eleven years. They died in the same year—2000. In between, their lives diverged quite dramatically.

Though they were only 2 years old when war broke out, the First World War had an immense effect on their lives and on the lives of their fellow islanders. On Saturday 2 August 1914, virtually the whole able-bodied male population of Lewis was called to join up immediately. In numerical terms this meant that of a total population of 29,603 a staggering 6,712 men joined up. Furthermore, some 1,151 men who did enlist lost their lives. This meant that there were virtually no fishermen left on the island—their nets were left drying in the fields and turned to relics. Fishing had been the most important occupation and a vital source of nutrition. With the male workforce absent for such a long time, the traditional crofting and fishing that had sustained the island never recovered. Duncan Duff wrote in Scotland's War Losses:

> If the ratio of the killed to the total population be considered, the island paid twice as much as the rest of the kingdom in its sacrifice.

Eventually the war did end and exhausted servicemen made the long journey home. At 2 am on the morning of 1 January 1919 His Majesty's Yacht *Iolaire* —the *Eagle*—was wrecked on a reef called the Beasts of Holm, only yards from the shore and within sight of Stornoway harbour. There were 283 men on board, including 205 World War One servicemen. The official death toll was put at 205. *The Scotsman* reported the tragedy on 6 January:

> The villages of Lewis are like places of the dead. The homes of the island are full of lamentation—grief that cannot be comforted. Scarcely a family has escaped the loss of a near blood relative. Many have had sorrow heaped upon sorrow.

After the war there followed a great wave of emigration from the islands to the United States and Canada. In the early 1920s, some 3,000 men emigrated from Lewis. They had, of course, been promised 'A Land fit for Heroes'. Instead, the Tory Prime Minister Stanley Baldwin encouraged them to find land in the colonies. This created even greater losses for the island.

The two girls, Christina Ann and Mary, were affected by all these events. In the early 1920s, four sisters and a brother of Christina Ann emigrated to Detroit. Mary had three sisters who also emigrated to the United States. While Christina Ann remained in the village all of her life, in 1930 Mary sailed to New York to join one of her sisters.

On the island, as in so many peasant communities, it was the women who were the beasts of burden. They were also expected to look after their ageing parents. This was to be Christina Ann's fate. A huge amount of physical work was done by the women. From the shores they collected seaweed, which was used as a fertiliser, and carried it in creels on their backs. They also carried peats home from peat banks in the same creels over long distances. When the men went out fishing, the women waded out to the boats carrying the fishermen on their backs so they would not get their feet wet. Boots were incredibly precious.

As the years passed, Christina Ann and Mary married. Christina Ann married a sailor returning from the Second World War and Mary married into a well-to-do New York family who made their money from property development. They both gave birth to a boy in 1946. There was a huge disparity in the lives that they led. Christina Ann continued living on her parents' croft, which was only connected to mains electricity in 1950. It was only used for lighting since peat provided fuel for heating and cooking, just as it had always done. Meanwhile, Mary was enjoying the New York high society life.

Over the years, Mary came back to the island on a regular basis to visit her family and friends, including Christina Ann. By the time they were widows, Christina Ann's life had become much more comfortable and she entertained Mary in her pebbledash croft house with home-made scones and tea served in pretty cups.

In the late 1970s, Christina Ann's oldest son married a lass from Aberdeenshire and he brought her to the island. Years later, when having a rummage, his lovely wife found an unexpected item of clothing. It was a

Pierre Cardin suit! They asked Christina Ann about it and she explained that the *'Peer Cardine'* was a gift from her friend Mary, who often brought her hand-me—downs on her visits to Lewis. She gave it to her daughter-in-law.

On 8 November 2016, 16 years after Mary passed away, her son became President of the United States of America. Meanwhile, Christina Ann's son was listening to Bob Dylan and ranting to anyone who would listen about the evils of capitalism.

Tom Hubbard

is a novelist, poet and semi-retired academic. His most recent book is *The Devil and Michael Scott: a Gallimaufry of Fife and Beyond* (Grace Note Publications, 2020). In 2017, also published by Grace Note, Tom brought out three novellas called *Slavonic Dances* and the collection *The Flechitorium*. He also contributed a poem to *A Kist of Thistles* in 2020 and brought out the same year *Not my Circus, Not my Monkey* along with Sheena Blackhall and published by Malfranteaux Concepts. Both his grandfathers howked coal in Fife; his paternal grandfather was determined that his two sons would not follow suit.

Grandads

My wife was taking a walk in Kirkcaldy's Beveridge Park when she met our friend David Potter, local historian and author. He told her that Kennedy's centenary was approaching.

'I didnae know David was interested in American politics,' said I. 'But wasn't Kennedy's centenary a few years back?'

'No—not JFK,' said my wife. 'He meant Tom Kennedy, who became Kirkcaldy's first Labour MP in March 1921.'

A native of Aberdeen, Kennedy served for a long time, eventually standing down in 1944 due to ill health. At the consequent by-election my grandfather, Tom Hubbard, became his successor, initially as a wartime coalition member, then in 1945 joining the mass intake of Labour MPs. His SNP opponent for the early contests was the eminent Scottish poet and classical scholar Douglas Young, who would become his friend. I inherited the typically quirky Christmas card which he sent my grandfather.

The historian Professor Christopher Harvie of Tübingen University wrote of my grandfather's candidature: 'A local miner, Councillor Tom Hubbard, had been adopted as a result, it was alleged, of a combination of communist and unionist machinations. The communists favoured him because he had supported C.P. affiliation to the Labour Party: the unionists (i.e. the Tories) supported him because he would prove a weak opponent once they were given a chance to contest.' As it happened, he beat off his Tory challengers in all subsequent elections until ill health forced him to withdraw before the 1959 election.

Tom Hubbard senior was born in 1898 in Cork of an Irish mother and an English father; they hailed respectively, from Co. Waterford and Surrey, so it was not inevitable that our tribe would become Scottish. At this time, the family was Catholic and large; my grandfather was the second of three brothers and he had four sisters. He married in 1922 and settled in Dysart, Fife, where most of the men went down the pit; it's now a gentrified suburb of Kirkcaldy. Wading through water and breathing in coal dust most likely contributed to his chronically poor health. He suffered from lumbago, rheumatism and diabetes; he was also a heavy smoker; when my childhood overlapped with his later years, my parents and I made many hospital visits.

During the Parliament of 1950-51, when Attlee's government struggled with a slim majority, my grandfather was carried on a stretcher into the House of Commons in order to cast his vote. He campaigned much on old age pensions and, aptly, on health issues, speaking much on pneumoconiosis, that scourge of the miners. He'd have been proud, had he lived longer, of a great-niece who became a doctor. When a stroke hit him, I was eight years old and was alarmed to see him writing on House of Commons notepaper about his condition; attempting to write 'burst blood vessel' he got the words mixed up because they both began with a b. He was the constituency's MP, but he was my grandad, and I didn't know what was happening to him. He died in 1961, aged 62.

In Parliament he jousted with Lady Tweedsmuir, the Tory MP for Aberdeen South and daughter-in-law of the novelist John Buchan. In response to another Tory, he displayed a blend of working-class decorum and cheek: 'I consider it ungentlemanly to say anything unkind to the Hon. Lady, so I will leave that task to some of my colleagues who are better fitted than I am for that kind of thing.'

In November 1957, and on a more serious, indeed sombre note, he addressed the House with this memory: 'In 1926, in common with all miners, I was locked out. My employers refused to continue my employment on the conditions that had been negotiated between miners and mine owners. I was disqualified, along with everybody else, from drawing unemployment benefit. Having a wife and two children, I qualified for public assistance.'

'We were compelled to live on 11s a week. That would have been bad enough had it been paid in cash, but the amount was given in the form of a voucher... When my wife went out to buy groceries, the grocer had to go to other shops and purchase her meat and bread for her. We got no change from those vouchers, which had to be spent in one shop. We could not go from one shop to another to purchase what we wanted. That horrible experience we had for seven months.'

Back in Kirkcaldy, and from a hospital bed, he gave me a Christmas present of two books in the American-published Classics Illustrated series. Today we'd call them graphic novels; my artist/designer daughter Claire (born 1989) would use the word 'comics' for a wider and more sophisticated range of publications. However, I grew up with Classics Illustrated and they introduced me to the real thing—literature.

My grandad's gifts, then, contributed to my own career as a man of letters. They were versions of Dickens' *Oliver Twist* and Henry Morton

Stanley's *How I Found Livingstone*. They proved to have a long reach: my most recent academic article was on Dickens and Dostoevsky. As for Stanley, it reflected my grandad's great interest in Africa; he was a member of parliamentary delegations to newly independent states such as Ghana (known as the Gold Coast until 1957) and Nigeria. I still have the Nigerian drum which he brought back for me.

My other grandad, Angus McKay, did not have such a public presence, and was still a miner during my childhood. I was about eight when I heard my dad saying that his father-in-law was 'a bit of a commie', whatever that meant. My only experience, such as it was, of working-class life was when I was being looked after in Linktown's Buchanan Street (since demolished) by my maternal grandparents at weekends or during odd weekdays. My aunt Jean is still with us at 89; she tells me that she and my mum, playing outside, had to go home for tea when they heard my grandad's boots in the street at the end of his shift. I myself remember his entrances, completely black, and my gran sending me through to the bedroom while he had his bath in the metal tub forenent the living room fireplace. When I was called back into the living room, he was sitting at the table, reading his paper, dapper in suit, white shirt and tie; the very essence of working-class respectability you might say, but his job made him value cleanliness. His hands, however, remained rough and blue—not black, but blue: a blue-black, more like. I think I never heard him swear; working life was coarse, leisure time was different, especially when I was in earshot.

During a family holiday we were staying in what may have been the mankiest hotel in Ostend, and witnessed the proprietor pissing in the corridor. With my then brand of adolescent humour, I suggested that we follow suit, but grandad insisted that 'we came here as gentlemen, we'll leave here as gentlemen.' Grandad had his own brand of cheek, dry, laconic, on the dour side but never malicious. He was warm-hearted and loving and I was devastated when, in 1967, aged 65, he died of cancer. I was sixteen at the time. If my grandads had made it to 70 (my age now) and beyond, I might have benefited from their guidance and reached a level of emotional maturity (always lower than its intellectual counterpart) much earlier than was the case.

The McKays' Buchanan Street flat had two rooms. The lavvy was an outside one, in what I may po-facedly have called the courtyard ('the carriage awaits, m'lord'). The smell was mingin, the seat wooden, but to a nail there was attached all that you needed immediately after a bodily function. I learned early that the tabloid press was good for at least two things, and one was to contain fish suppers.

Grandad McKay, like Grandad Hubbard, had lived in Dysart, from where they went down the pit, and where their respective daughter and son met and courted. I owe my very existence to coal, but now I listen to the warnings of Greta Thunberg, who is much younger than my three bairns. I remember old integrities but must now support the new.

John Cassidy

grew up in a room and kitchen on the top floor of a tenement building in Bridgeton, Glasgow. Gaining an apprenticeship in Howden's as a boilermaker, he went on to become a quality control inspector at John Brown Engineering before his first stint as a further education lecturer. After returning to industry for a short time, including running his own company, John went back to work at Cardonald College, Glasgow, as a lecturer in fabrication and welding. He is a past President of the Educational Institute of Scotland (College Lecturers' Association), being awarded a Fellowship of the EIS in 2003. He was also awarded an MBE in 2006.

The Life of a Clydebuilt Apprentice

1960/61

I was very fortunate to get a job when I left school. The main reason I got a chance was my family had strong ties with the famous Glasgow engineering company James Howden, Scotland Street. In those days, if you had someone who could 'speak' for you, it helped. At that time there were not many working-class people who went on to higher education. In fact, it was considered an achievement if you got a trade.

My brother Pat got me an application form to sit the exam to become an office boy. I was very nervous when I sat the exam in May 1960; prior to that, the only other exam I had sat was the now discredited 'Qualie'. Two weeks later I got a letter telling me I had passed the exam and I should come to see them with details of what they had in store for me. I went in to see the personnel manager on Friday 3 July. However, it was not straightforward, there was a slight hitch. The date that I had to start was the first Monday after the Glasgow Fair. The problem was, I would not be eligible to leave school then as I was only fourteen and could not leave school until November. This meant I had lost my job before I had started. They sympathised, but told me to keep in touch as they could not keep the job open for me. So, keep in touch I did.

As November approached, I was beginning to lose hope. When I phoned on Monday 31 October, they told me to come in to see them on the Wednesday. I could hardly wait and was nice and early for my 8.30 am appointment, only to be told that the personnel manager did not start until nine. When I got into the meeting, the lasting impression I had of this man offering me a 'start' the following Monday without looking at me was that he was too busy reading his paper, the Herald. However, I later learned that he was checking to see if all his job adverts had been inserted into that day's edition of the paper. It transpired that the reason I was given the job was that some boy had betrayed their trust and had been 'bagged' for stealing. So off I set on the work experience part of life a long time ago.

The other momentous event that occurred that week, although not just so important, was the election of John F. Kennedy as President of the USA. I worked away busily and eager to please right through to my holidays on the Glasgow Fair.

1961/62

When I returned from my holidays, spent in Arbroath, I had another week as an office boy to show the new recruit the ropes, including how to 'skin' the tea fund, then it was off to the apprentice school. At the outset no-one was given any particular trade to follow as the management said that they wanted to assess what we were best at before they decided which trade we were best suited for. What they were actually doing was waiting to see what the company's requirements would be in the years ahead.

This was the first time, apart from school classrooms, I had been involved with a large group of thirty-two boys. I lived so far from my school, due to having passed the qualifying exam, which determined the school I had to attend, that I had to run for the bus before my travel pass expired, so I had no time to socialise with any of the boys I was frequently with at school. You have to remember that only about ten boys from each Primary 7 class passed the dreaded 'Qualie', enabling them to attend a senior secondary school.

However, my fears were unfounded; they were a great crowd of boys. In fact, they were so good they spoiled it for those who followed. The reason for this was the firm gave various concessions such as afternoon football, no loss of pay for pass outs, and a weekly trip to the swimming baths. This trip to the baths was a twofold exercise. Then, not everyone stayed in a house with a bath, so it made sure we had one good wash each week. Well, what happened? No-one spoiled it; everyone went to play football; not too many pass outs were used; and we all walked along to the baths in all types of weather throughout the year. So, what did the firm do? The next year they didn't offer any concessions because they couldn't cast up 'You spoil everything you get!'

We finished the year off going on holiday to Great Yarmouth.

1962/63

When I started back to work after my holiday, I began my apprenticeship proper. I was to be a plater. A plater is the same as a joiner except that he uses steel/metal as opposed to wood.

If I was surprised at the religious bigotry in the offices, although there was none in the apprentice school, I was astonished at the extent of it on the shop floor. It transpired that I was the first Catholic apprentice plater to start in twenty years. I tackled the situation the only way I knew—that was head on. I didn't deny what I was, nor did I boast. I just treated people as I found them.

Howden's, being a traditional workshop, had football as its main obsession. All the apprentices and a lot of the young tradesmen played for teams. Every Monday was taken up with their boasts as to how well they had played, but I was virtually ignored as I was considered only a wee boy, as I was still only sixteen. Then, about two months later, my status changed dramatically. At the end of the Monday shift I went in to wash my hands when Willie Clark, one of the respected tradesmen, asked me if he had seen me playing for Shettleston Juniors on Saturday. By the time I had finished drying my hands, I was the talk of the 'Steamie'. To play Junior in those days carried a bit of prestige. From that day, I jumped up several rungs of the ladder.

I was also introduced to the cruelty and insensitivity of workshop culture by the way in which initiation ceremonies were carried out on new apprentices and in pre-stag frolics. Boys were stripped naked, greased, tied to a stretcher and left lying in the middle of the street. Young men the night before their wedding would be painted, you know where, with red lead on engineers' blue, which would take hours of scrubbing to get clean enough for bedtime. Whether they were fit enough after all that scrubbing was another matter, but as most of them had done the damage already, I don't suppose it mattered. The favourite stag night in Howden's was to go to the pub, then go on to the Pavilion to see Lex McLean and then back to the intended's house for an all-night bevvie session. The pubs closed at 9.30 pm then.

By the time 1963 came in, I was well-established and doing all sorts of things to earn money. However, I didn't save any, I just used it to subsidise trips to the café for the other apprentices. In a good week, we would 'climb the wall' and go over to Lewis's to listen to the latest records, then go somewhere for lunch. I made the money by running sweepstakes and organising a 'tick' line in the shop that sold pieces and cigarettes. The thing that amused me was that these men were doing two nights and a Sunday, and yet, on the Sunday or Monday after getting a good day's pay, they would need tick to buy cigarettes the rest of the week. In fact, I made so much money from the various lines that the tradesmen came to me for a loan.

One of the reasons they came to me was that I did not charge interest like the 'tally men'; there were a couple of real heavies who loaned money in Howden's then. One time a young tradesman came begging me for a loan, as he had a date. I didn't have any money, but he started to plead. He was so desperate to get money that he either held her in high regard or low esteem.

He kept begging, so I asked him for a loan of his watch for half an hour and I'd see what I could do. True to my word, I was back within half an hour and had managed to get him £2. He asked how I managed to get the money and what about his watch? I gave him his pawn ticket and told him to redeem it on Friday, and then ran before his boot caught me.

1963/64

After the annual holiday, I was back to the grind. I had started to play football with Arthurlie, and it was that season we were involved in a round of the Scottish Cup that needed four games to complete. It was against Petershill, who were the favourites, and it started on the first Saturday of December, at home. As usual for a Cup-tie, there was a reasonable crowd of 2,000, but the game ended 0-0. As there was a terrible freeze in Glasgow, the next Saturday every Senior game was off, but Junior ties just ignored the conditions; the game must go on.

You can imagine the atmosphere when we went on to the field with over 10,000 in the crowd to see the replay. My father went to see me that day, and he met his foreman from work. The gaffer knew my father very seldom went to see games, and asked him what he was doing in this neck of the woods watching the Peasies. Without waiting for an answer, he shouted *'Get that dirty big bastard off the park! He was at it last week as well.'* My dad told him he was up to see his boy play.

'Which player is he?' asked the gaffer.
'The one you're just after shouting at,' my dad replied.

That game also ended 0-0. The third game was played at Pollok's ground and it had a crowd of 25,000. It finished 2-2 after extra time and with ten-a-side, as a man from each side had been ordered off. The fourth game, again at Pollok, ended in a 4-0 defeat, but it was great while it lasted. Virtually everyone in Howden's was following it with great interest, either going to the game or looking out for the score. The next game, it was back to reality; we played Vale of Leven away, and in front of twenty-four people.

1964/65

For all I was progressing with my apprenticeship, I still had two years to go, so there was still time for me to enjoy myself. One day, a younger boy and I 'jumped the wall', but on our way back in we were spied by a gaffer. It was in the dispatch department. A large job that had been created ready for dispatch stood between us and a clean escape. We jumped behind the crate to hide.

The gaffer jumped behind the crate on the other side to try to capture us. It was like the Keystone Cops running round the crate, trying to keep two sides between us. To shake him off, we climbed on top of the crate. It was funny to see how he searched for us, looking to see where we had gone.

I had my first taste of wage negotiations that year. Apprentices did not have a voice on the wages panel. I was lucky to be involved. I was still not the oldest boy in the fan shop, but I objected to the settlement. The agreed deal was five shillings per hour for skilled workers and three shillings for unskilled, with both getting an extra tanner (sixpence) per hour for giving up their tea break. The apprentices got a shilling, and nothing for giving up their tea break. As the tradesmen's extra tanner per hour was for giving up the afternoon tea break I told the convener, the chief shop steward of the whole factory, that as we apprentices had given up the same tea break, we were entitled to the same tanner. If there was no discrimination between skilled and unskilled workers, it wasn't fair to discriminate against us. He said that if I felt so strongly about it, I should approach management. His tone was condescending. I was so annoyed that I called a meeting for apprentices that day.

The oldest boy in the fan shop reneged on representing us, so I went in with the two oldest engineers to meet with management. I don't know if they wanted to intimidate us, but they summoned us to the works manager's room. I put forward the case that because we were being denied the tea break, we were entitled to the same tanner per hour. After some to-ing and fro-ing, he eventually offered thruppence per hour. I refused. As you see, I ended up being the spokesperson. However, the others accepted and I was outvoted, so we had to accept. Nevertheless, it was not too bad a piece of negotiation.

1965/66

I returned to work after the holidays to start the final year of my apprenticeship. I took the decision, after an injury, to opt out of football in order to dedicate myself to my day-release college work. Instead of training, I did my homework, and it proved, just as in sport, if you put in the work, you'll get results. I gave up all of my scams to earn extra money, and as I had trained up the younger apprentices on how to do the scams properly, I let them get on with it. I took my trade seriously and successfully completed my City and Guilds course. Then, to crown it all, in March 1966 Harold Wilson called a General Election to increase his majority in the House of Commons. Labour was returned with a majority of ninety-seven. Folks like me thought at last we were going to have a true socialist society with a fairer distribution of wealth. Unfortunately, we are still waiting.

David Betteridge

formerly a teacher and teacher-trainer, has been writing since his twenties, but without publishing until his sixties, when his 'Five Glasgow Poems' appeared in *Cencrastus* (2002). Since then three books of poems have followed (with Smokestack Books and Culture Matters), and fourteen poetry pamphlets (Rhizome Press). Latterly, with Bob Starrett and Owen McGuigan, he has experimented with mixing poems, prose and images, inspired by John Berger's work.

Rediscovering the Best Part: UCS at 50

We are witnessing an eruption not of lava but of labour... the labour of working men and women.

—Jimmy Reid
Speech made on Glasgow Green,
18 August 1971

It is not every day, or every decade, that we take on capitalism and win, but that is what happened in 1971-72, when the workforce of the Upper Clyde Shipbuilders consortium occupied their yards, and, in so doing, fought off Edward Heath's government's intended butchery-by-closure. The workers asserted their right to work as a political principle as well as a here-and-now demand, and in doing so they gained worldwide support. Collectively, for a while, they fulfilled a vanguard role in the class war.

Their achievement was to keep their part of Clydeside from being made a desert. What is more they showed other trade unionists in dispute how to resist, and where the weak points of capitalism were. Scores of other workplace occupations followed. A shudder ran through the land as ruling elites felt the tectonic plates of their world begin to shift. Help! A subaltern class is not supposed to act like this.

The UCS workforce who achieved this epoch-making effect was only 8,000-plus strong, but their force was made many times stronger by the very numerous networks of support that we gave them locally (that is to say on Clydeside), across Scotland (encouraged by the STUC), and also across the whole of Britain and the wider world (demonstrating working class and trade union solidarity on an epic scale). Sometimes support came from less-than-obvious quarters. Famously, John Lennon and Yoko Ono gave the work-in's fighting fund the gift of a bunch of red roses, complemented by money. (Their highly relevant anthem 'Imagine' was released shortly after). Less famously, but just as worthily, local children held back-court concerts as fundraising events. The Royal Shakespeare Company sent a message expressing solidarity.

Briar by Bob Starrett

It fell to me, as a young teacher working in Scunthorpe at the time, to come to the shipyard gates at John Brown's in Clydebank with our donation, collected for the UCS fighting fund by our Scunthorpe Trades Council, on which I served as a delegate from the National Union of Teachers. Ushered through the gates by a steward, I was taken to what seemed to be the operations hub of the work-in, for that is what the workers' operation was, a 'work-in,' a new term for a new weapon in the waging of class struggle. The basic premise was to continue building the ships already under construction, or on the order book, but under workers' control, thereby denying the then Tory government any chance of overseeing the selling off of UCS assets to other firms, which was their sly plan.

The plan failed. The Government was forced to think again and do a U-turn, investing sufficiently in UCS to secure a future for it, intact. What was worse, from their point of view, the Government had to pause certain industrial relations 'reforms' that they had in mind, designed to strengthen employers' hands and weaken workers'.

'We all walked taller then,' as Jimmy Cloughley, one of the UCS stewards, said later, looking back at the inspired and inspiring struggle that he had been part of:

> We said No to the destruction of our communities, refusing to stop work... instead of meekly accepting the economic and political facts of life, and joining the dole queue.

Ann Henderson, who later on was Secretary to the STUC Women's Committee, summed up the work-in's legacy as follows, looking back at it from the standpoint of its fortieth anniversary:

> The action taken by the UCS workforce... ensured hope and work for thousands of workers and their families... We must revive those campaign skills, energy and co-ordination, and the legacy of a movement which put people before profit.

Also looking back at the work-in, but from the standpoint of fifty years on, the historian John Foster had this to say:

> The stewards had a strategy. It was based on a concrete, Marxist (yes, Marxist) analysis of the weakness of the Government's position and the potential strength of their own.

My visit to John Brown's was an eye-, mind-, and vision-opener. I saw workers' power actually existing, up and running, not just talked about or read about in a history book. I saw workers' power informed by a hard-headed (and hard-hatted) practicality *and* by a generous-hearted social ethic, in a winning combination. That social ethic was spelled out in a speech by the work-in's most prominent leader and spokesperson, Jimmy Reid, one of a leadership collective of the highest calibre. To an audience of university students and staff, when he was elected Rector of Glasgow University, he stated:

> To measure social progress purely by material advance is not enough. Our aim must be the enrichment of the whole quality of life. It requires a social and cultural, or if you wish, a spiritual transformation of our country.

Back home in Scunthorpe, in Labour Party and WEA study groups, and at union and Trades Council meetings, and also privately, trying to interpret this glimpse of history-in-the-making, and weigh its achievements against its inherent limitations, I arrived at the following conclusion, as did millions: the work-in compressed into one action a number of elements not always present in industrial disputes, in a unique deployment. What were these elements?

First, there was intelligence in reading the balance of power within and between classes, reflecting a Marxist perspective born of both experience and study.

Second, there was decisiveness in shifting from a war of position (entailing debates, policy-making, campaigning, etc.) to a war of manoeuvre (entailing work-place occupation and mobilising practical support from that new, stronger position).

Third, there was competence in organising the work-in, day after day over more than a year, as well as organising the building of the ships.

Fourth, there was skill in maintaining solidarity, in large part through good communications, including oratory at key moments by key players in the unfolding drama.

In my musings on the matter, I found Antonio Gramsci's writings to be helpful, in particular his *Prison Notebooks*. In one entry, commenting on solidarity and good communications, he noted that the socialist newspaper *L'Ordine Nuovo* had great appeal for many Turin workers in the dangerous years of 1919-22:

> Why? Because in its articles they rediscovered a part, the best part, of themselves... because the articles were virtually a 'taking note' of actual events, seen as moments of a process of inner liberation and self-expression on the part of the working class.

Does this explain in part the similar great impact of certain speeches by Jimmy Reid fifty years later, and also speeches by other eloquent members of the work-in's co-ordinating committee, including Jimmy Airlie? Chik Collins, who has written on the matter, thinks so. Regarding 'the speech of his life' that Reid delivered on Friday 24 September 1971, Chik Collins wrote:

> Some of those who attended the meeting spoke of a reaction to Reid's oratory which was as much physiological as intellectual— 'you could feel the hairs standing up on the back of your neck,' said Bob Dickie, another of the stewards.

The meeting in question was crucial in maintaining a 'four yards unity' when the Government came along with a divide-and-rule proposal that two yards might be saved if the workforce agreed to sacrifice two. Here (below) is the nub of Reid's appeal for unity, applicable to all times, and all situations, surely:

> It's like a murderer who wants to murder us, we've found out... we've defended ourselves against the murder and people say 'please negotiate with the murderer, you might stop him from piercing your heart, but he can cut off your legs and arms, and there's a sensible compromise.' And when you're lying bleeding, they will tell you in a year or two, wi' you minus the legs, why aren't you standing on your own two feet?

How closely this 'minus the legs' scenario resembles the sorts of cartoons that Bob Starrett draws, who drew cartoons at the time of the work-in for its *Bulletin!* How graphic it is in its imagery; and how powerful in its use of a language that Brecht called 'gestic'. The very ordering of the words paints the picture and enacts the drama being held up as a parable.

Where did these statesmen of the yards—Reid, Airlie, and the others —acquire their necessary skills and knowledge? That is the question. Partly, I think they acquired them from their total immersion in the yards, and in the unions, and in their working-class hinterland and history; but immersion is not sufficient. Lessons learned informally must be firmed up, and tempered into weapons of thought and structures of feeling that can withstand prolonged battering. It was through their membership of the CPGB and involvement in all its educational and cultural activities over many years that Reid and Airlie and a critical mass of other workers achieved this firming and tempering. It was a long labour.

There is a portrait of Reid, commissioned by his daughter for his 75th birthday, that gives us a hint of the great weight and variety of past influences operating on one brain, and one heart. The artist, Barry Atherton, places his subject at the centre of a storm of people and books, all influential in shaping him, some by good example, some by bad, others by just being there as subjects of reflection. We see Keir Hardie, John Maclean, Willie Gallacher, Mary Barbour, Helen Crawfurd, Joseph Stalin, Ramsay MacDonald, and Aneurin Bevan, politicians; we see comrades of his from the work-in, and family members; we see Adam Smith, Karl Marx and David Hume, philosophers, plus another of these troublesome thinkers, in statue form, standing just behind him, who is clearly an ancient Greek, probably Socrates; we see Robert Burns, his favourite poet; and we see piles of books and cascades of leaflets, a small selection from the library loads that Reid mastered. He believed and practised what Lenin was vehement in urging, that we make the breadth and depth of existing knowledge our own, 'from the bottom up', and then advance from there.

One book in the portrait catches my eye, a collection of Bob Starrett's cartoons, called *Rattling the Cage*, which I helped him prepare for publication some years after the work-in. Later, I collaborated again with this latter-day Eccles or Gabriel of Clydeside, and with the singer-songwriter Ewan McVicar. Together, we compiled a second book, *A Rose Loupt Oot*, calling on other comrades to contribute poems and songs to it. Like *Rattling*, this book also featured—in fact centred on—the work-in, looking back on it from forty years later, and finding its legacy still potent.

A portrait similar to that of Atherton's Reid could be painted for many others who made up the 8,000-plus workforce of the work-in, and the many more who made up their legions of allies, and also those activists who came after them. All of them contain multitudes. In preparing to write this piece, I consulted some of them, starting with Jimmy Cloughley and Bob Starrett, already mentioned, and also Andy Sanders, Danny McCafferty and Jimmy McGeachy. They gave me a treasury of insights and memories, sufficient for a fat book. Here is a small sample of what they told me in answer to my inquiry about the sources of their own skills and knowledge:

> My political education came from the likes of Finlay Hart, Jock Smith, Alec Annan, Johnny Gill, John Tonner, Mary McGuire, Betty McGeachy, May Halfpenny and many other Bankies... too many to mention (We learned) sometimes through practice... other elements through theory...
> The shipyards were in that period places where there were men knowledgeable in most things...
> My dad was Literature Secretary for the Babcock branch of the party. My mother still has a trunk of books in the attic of old Left Book Club stuff dating back to then...

I heard Jimmy mention *How the Steel was Tempered* by Nikolae Ostrovsky. A quote from the novel was printed on the front of our YCL cards:

'Man's dearest possession is life.'

I think we all read widely, especially American literature —Steinbeck (Grapes of Wrath, In Dubious Battle, etc.) and Jack London, Mick McGahey's favourite. Also Sinclair Lewis (Main Street and Babbitt). James Barke's Major Operation was also known, possibly the most political Scottish novel apart from A Scot's Quair...

Mary McGuire encouraged the youth. She held YCL fund-raising socials in her own house, complete with home-made bar...

It all seems so long ago, probably because it is! Funny to think what a wonderful educational forum the YCL and CP were: we had classes in Economics, Politics, Literature (Honor Arundel took those), Education (Brian Simon), Public Speaking, and all the time out on the streets, round the doors, and at union meetings, also Trades Council, CND, Gay Rights... and just about everything else you could think of...

Naming these names is important—and there are screeds of other names deserving of recognition, Sammy Barr, for instance, and George Kerr, and Davie Cooper, and Sammy Gilmore, stewards eloquent in furthering the work-in through its ups and downs—because doing so reminds us of the hydra-headed nature of any cultural formation, and its reliance on complex networks of learning and influence. What a rich soil, to change the metaphor, the work-in drove its deep and spreading roots into!

But now? Here we are, in 2021, with a right-wing coup under way and us giving too little resistance to it. How can we recover the fighting spirit of the work-in of half a century ago? What lessons are there that we can derive, adapt and apply to these changed circumstances? Maybe, if a composite Ghost of Actions Past might speak, it might say:

Do not underestimate the enemy, who have out-classed us down the ages, maintaining their property rights and their rule over us; but do not overestimate them, either.

Build and rebuild and extend—like a spider working on its web—both union and party, and community and nation, throwing multiple cross-links to others.

Get the boxes of books down from the attic; re-read them, and then write your own; similarly with films, songs, and art-works of all kinds, packing into them all you know plus all you imagine, thus creating a culture that makes sense of your lives, and educates desire.

Emulate the briar, digging down deep with your

sustenance-seeking roots, and climb high towards future's light, spiralling up and up, following a trajectory similar to Tatlin's Tower and similar to the briar's, making sure that your older, stronger, jaggier shoots support the younger ones.

Even in the present valley of the shadow, prepare for government, and with it good governance, too.

William Hershaw

is a Scots language poet, playwright, singer and musician. He is a member of the editorial board of *Lallans*. He is the founder of the folk group The Bowhill Players who perform music celebrating Fife's coal mining culture. In 2018 he wrote *The Sair Road*, his Scots language version of *The Stations of the Cross* set during the 1984 miners' strike. His poems and songs have been widely published and recorded both in Scotland and abroad. In 2021 Grace Notes will publish two new collections of poetry: *Saul Vaigers—A Scottish Saints' Calendar* and *Earth Bound Companions* in conjunction with Les McConnell.

Birlan—The 1984-85 Miners' Strike in Scotland

During the 1984-85 miners' strike I was a young teacher, just out of probation, in Kirkcaldy. It was a time when the political views I hold to this day were formed. Having been brought up in the bubble of a coal mining family in a coal mining community I supported the miners' cause unquestioningly and emotionally. Well versed in the lore of previous industrial struggles involving the NUM, it was obvious, I thought, who had the moral right and it was from that perspective that I saw the whole conflict. By the end of it, the fight had been lost, but so had my trust and faith.

The Thatcher Government had previously announced their intention to close 20 pits across Britain with another 70 under review of closure. By this time, the coal mining industry in the UK had been in considerable decline for decades. Yet there were numerous towns, villages and communities across the country that owed their existence to King Coal. In these places, the infrastructure of the whole community depended on the local pit. There were still 202,000 employed in the industry at the outbreak of the strike— a considerable amount, though nothing like the 1,191,000 employed at the industry's peak in 1920.

In Scotland there were only around 13,000 miners (compared with 56,000 in Yorkshire). The Lanarkshire coalfield, the biggest and most productive in Scotland, had been all but exhausted by the end of WW2. In my hometown of Cowdenbeath, the last pit had closed as far back as 1963. Yet despite the steady drop in its membership, the NUM still exerted a symbolic significance as a totem of the workers' solidarity and strength due to its historic role in fighting to protect jobs and communities—in recent memory it had brought down the Heath Government in 1971. Thatcher's intention was to destroy the power and influence of the trade unions in order to implement a monetarist plan for Britain's future. The miners had to be supported at all costs, Thatcherism had to be resisted.

It was a great shock to me when it became apparent that many people did not agree with my view of things. In fact, there was a range of opinion, including many Labour voting trade unionists, who qualified their support for the miners or even refused it. Some agreed with Thatcher that the miners' strike was illegal. As the strike drew out to its bitter end in March 1985, certainly within Fife, there was plenty sympathy for the hardship endured by striking miners and especially their families, but donations to the soup kitchen never translated into anything like full unconditional political support for their action to save jobs and therefore communities—even within some of these same communities. Gallup polls conducted during the strike show that at no point did the miners enjoy a majority of support from the British public and what public support they had eroded as the strike went on. The position of the Labour opposition leader Neil Kinnock, who represented a coal mining area and whose grandfather had been a coal miner, said that he supported 'the case for coal' while opposing the tactics and methods of Scargill's NUM. This seam of ambivalence permeated the strata of the Labour movement and arguably still does.

Nobody seemed to be discussing the big picture: the job losses, the closures, the lack of viable alternatives, and the ensuing poverty. Most of all, nobody seemed to recognise that unlike previous politicians who pursued short-term agendas, Thatcher was attempting permanent changes to British society through her vicious right-wing agenda of law changes, deregulation, privatisation, backed up with a programme of removing the rights of workers and citizens. She was putting ideology and economics before people. This is not hindsight—she was saying at the time what she wanted to do and many people lapped up what they were hearing.

I remember hearing continuously the *Daily Mail* mantra that the miners' actions were undemocratic and illegal because the miners' leader, Arthur Scargill, had refused to hold a strike ballot. Scargill had not called the strike in the first place. (It had started as a unilateral walkout at Cortonwood Colliery in Yorkshire). What quickly became apparent was that he had given his opponents a stick with which to baton the miners with. The alacrity with which they wielded it was alarming. He had also allowed fence sitters with an excuse. Sadly, they shook their heads. 'If only he wasn't such a loose cannon, I could have supported the miners!'

The other aspect that the media focused on, including the supposedly unbiased BBC, was to present negative news images of picketing miners, depicting them as violent thugs in donkey jackets, attacking the police, rioting and destroying and vandalising their very places of employment. I knew this not to be the truth from reports from my Uncle Wullie, who had been arrested on the Longannet picket line and spent a night in the cells. There was little attempt made to explain rationally or analyse the reasons for the strike taking place. Yet anyone who lived in a coal mining community knew what was going to happen if the local pit closed—poverty and deprivation on a scale unheard of would, and did ensue. By the end of the strike, in Cowdenbeath unemployment stood at 20%. There was nothing to replace the dinosaur industry.

I never suffered unduly as a teacher during the miners' strike. Kirkcaldy was not a predominantly mining town. The Nairns company who famously floored an empire with their linoleum was the main employer at that time. There were a number of families whose fathers worked at Seafield, which extended under the Forth, or the always-flooding Frances Colliery, nicknamed 'The Dubbie', in Dysart. I was never arrested for breach of the peace on the picket line. Or thrown into the back of a police van and beaten up. I was never given a criminal record, or lost my job, or pension. I never had to go hungry, get into debt, or was unable to provide for my family. But plenty miners experienced these things.

The worst thing that happened to me was when I announced I was intending to take an afternoon off work to attend a march along Kirkcaldy esplanade in support of the miners. I was a member of the EIS and I cannot remember if this was considered to be secondary picketing or not. I had no dealings with the Deputy Rector up until then. He appeared at assemblies as a genial older man with a red nose. I was told that he was a member of the Labour Party with a lot of influence locally. I was not worried when I was asked to go to his office. He was responsible for organising cover for absent teachers and my absence, it turned out, would cause him a small amount of work.

I can still remember the ferocity with which he launched into me. If I did not turn up to teach my classes the next day, he informed me, he would notify the Director of Education at Fife House, he would have my contract brought out and he would have me sacked for breach of it. Young and tongue-tied, I left his office shaking. All these years later I remember it vividly. I understand now that he was trying to intimidate me. I went on the march though. When I returned to school the next day, deeply worried, nothing more was said about it. Such experiences are formative in setting your views, in aligning your political compass. During this time, Fife was known as a Labour fiefdom from top to bottom. The teaching profession was no different. In fact, I was given the advice to join the Labour Party as 'it would help my career.' Yet I heard plenty Labour men criticise the miners, their leaders and the strike itself during this time.

But this is old history. Why dig it up? We wouldn't want the filthy pits back now anyway, so how is it relevant?

In October 2018, the Scottish Government published the findings of its independent review of the policing of the miners' strike in Scotland between the years 1984-5 and its impact on communities. Its recommendation was that men convicted for matters related to the strike be pardoned. The report recognised that in Scotland at least, during the strike, the Thatcher Government, the judiciary and the police had acted concertedly and often unjustly against the National Union of Mineworkers.

It is to the credit of the Scottish Parliament that the review happened. In January 2014, the then Prime Minister David Cameron dismissed a Labour call for him to apologise to the former mining communities for Thatcher's conspiracy to destroy the miner's union with the subsequent devastating effect of job losses on mining communities. 'If anyone should apologise, it's Arthur Scargill for his appalling leadership,' was his haughty retort. In 2016, the then Home Secretary Amber Rudd rejected the possibility of an inquiry into Orgreave. 'It's not like Hillsborough. Nobody died,' was the Tory line. Three people did. But tens of thousands were affected.

As part of the review process, meetings were held across Scotland in former coal mining areas to allow those involved to give their personal accounts. I attended the Lochgelly meeting. I found it an emotional experience and one that brought the anger back. The phone tapping, the traps set by police, the brutality, the collusion between the Coal Board, the police and the judiciary, the vindictiveness in sentencing, and all this to serve the sociopathic ideology of Thatcher, friend of Pinochet, opposer of sanctions on the South African apartheid regime. Listening to men, most of them elderly now, telling their stories about what had happened to them, how they had been treated and how their lives had been adversely and permanently affected, I realised that they had been abandoned.

One guy got up and told his story. He looked too young. His name was Wattie, and he was the youngest miner in the UK to be convicted. He had just started down the pit and was 17. Heading along the road to join his mates on the picket line, a police van had passed him. Like a daft laddie, he had given the van a V-sign. It stopped, and three burly policemen got out and shoved him in their van. He was arrested and charged. On appearing at Dunfermline Sheriff Court he was given this advice: 'Plead guilty, son. Do this and you'll just get a fine and can go home. If not, you'll have to be remanded in Saughton for a fortnight.' Terrified, he went along with it. He took a bus home from the court to find that a brown envelope had already been stuffed through his letterbox, unstamped. It was from the Coal Board, informing him that he had been sacked. As if they knew the conviction outcome already. Wattie had never been in trouble before and hasn't been since.

Listening to the victims of the strike speaking with a rawness and hurt and anger made me realise that for them it was a still present reality and not something that had faded with time. How could it be when they were still technically labelled as criminals? It brought back to me how much I had forgotten but also a realisation that the miners' strike was a fork in the road.

Collectively, we had taken the wrong path and in the ensuing years moved further away from the better one. To flog a metaphor to death, was it possible at this juncture to get back on the right one without retracing our steps?

More thoughts came back: my miner grandad Comp was more of a political observer. A canny old fox. He had been a member of the Independent Labour Party as a younger man, but he had communist sympathies. He had grown disillusioned. He worked back shift in Glencraig and then High Valleyfield, which meant that he left for the pit at the back of one and returned home at ten to get his tatties and stew. Sometimes in the mornings he would teach me how to play dominoes and cards or let me help him water his tomatoes. On these occasions, he would read his paper and share some of his thoughts with me. He had a tin of tobacco which fascinated me, and he rolled up his own fags with Rizla paper. They popped up as if by magic.

Mainstream Labour could not be trusted, he told me. They would make all sorts of promises to improve the lot of the common worker, but once they were voted in, they would disappear into the House of Commons, enjoy a soft easy London life like Jennie Lee in Mayfair and do absolutely nothing. But his hypocrite in chief was someone called Manny Shinwell who had initially been a red Clydeside firebrand whom he heard speaking at public meetings during the hungry twenties along with James Maxton. Manny had later veered sharply to the right upon his elevation to the peerage. I took all this in. This was long before Tony Blair and Gordon Brown. This was before Gorbals Mick Martin, Baron of Springburn, who became Speaker of the House of Commons in his tights and gown. This was before Lords Foulkes and McConnell and all the other parades of pathetic scunners who continue to fulfil my grandfather's prophecy.

The Tories, he told me, were the natural enemies of the working class as wasps were to aphids. They owned everything, and they intended to hang on to it by all the means they had—which were considerable. They were selfish, greedy, and uncaring, so you knew where you stood with them. The really privileged ones had no real idea what the life of the poor was like. As a young man in Lanark, he had attended a political meeting and listened to a speech by a young Tory named Alexander Douglas Home. At the end, for a laugh, a well-read miner schooled in Workers' Educational night classes and Marxist theory put his hand up and in a thick yokel accent said that he had heard tell of a proposal to turn the whole of the Highlands into banana plantations. Did the worthy gentleman think this a workable solution to create employment and reverse the effects of the Clearances? 'A capital idea! Splendid!' beamed the future Prime Minister of the UK condescendingly, 'I'll take that back to HQ.'

Liberals were not to be countenanced according to Comp. They were kind of snaky, ferret creatures whose danger lay in their wily espousal of reasonable-sounding hail-fellow-well-met policies when in reality they were Tories in disguise. They pretended to be your pal. Nor did Comp trust the SNP, although he had nothing against the idea of independence. Comp was a Catholic with Irish ancestry. At that time it was thought that the Labour Party, for all its hypocrisy, looked after Catholics better than the other parties. The SNP by definition were Scottish, and Scottish meant Protestant. You just had to look at Billy Wolfe and Gordon Wilson, their right-leading leaders.

But does any of this matter now? Thatcherism not only cursed working-class communities with material poverty but in the longer term with a crippling cultural poverty that removed aspiration and hope from generations of youngsters. In the latter part of my teaching career, I witnessed its effects in Methil and Cowdenbeath. If politics is defined as 'the art of the possible' then the miners' strike confirmed me as a Yes voter for Scottish independence.

Scotland Past has long gone but Scotland Present is a direct result of the political choices taken then. We've drifted more and more to the right, away from the traditional communal values of caring for each other espoused and practised in the former mining communities. The miners' strike came just five years after the first failed Devolution Referendum. That time a ballot was held, but it was effectively fixed by an amendment from George Cunningham, a Scottish Labour MP for Islington South and Finsbury, requiring 40% of the electorate for a Scottish Parliament to be set up. In the end, Donald Dewar's attempt to buy the Scottish people off with a kid on reservation talking shop back-fired and led to increased demands for independence and the rise of the SNP as a left of centre party (not a socialist one though).

But independence does provide hope of a change of political direction. Socialism may be dead, though I hope not, but even a workhouse with a kinder face would be a step in the right direction in the present climate. And who would want to stop this? Well, apparently, not only the owners of the banana plantations but the Labour Party, thirled to not only preventing independence but to the fundamentally undemocratic position of denying the Scottish people even a say in their own future. And all so that Keir Starmer and his crew, having undermined Jeremy Corbyn, the most socialist leader they have had in decades, can get in at Westminster and be the new Tories!

In 1984 the UK Government launched a planned co-ordinated attack on its own people for the sake of a right wing ideology. But the miners were never considered by the Tories as their own people any more than working-class Scots are today. It happened again when the Little Englanders engineered their Brexit. It will happen in the future if we allow it. It will continue so long as we allow ourselves to be governed by a class who do not share our belief that people and their lives are worth more than the accumulation of wealth and status. If you hold still to the now much undermined belief that:

> For a' that, an a' that,
> Our toils obscure an a' that,
> The rank is but the guinea's stamp,
> The Person's the gowd for a' that.

Then you have no other choice. Sometimes you need to birl in order to get back to where you were.

Allan Armstrong

is a communist, republican socialist, Scottish internationalist and freethinker. He has written *From Davitt to Connolly* and *The Ghost of James Connolly*. Allan also publishes books and articles online at https://intfrobel.com and is on the editorial board of *Emancipation, Liberation and Self-Determination* (http://republicancommunist.org/ blog. He is a contributor to *Bella Caledonia* (https://bellacaledonia.org.uk/contributor /allan-armstrong/) and to several books including *Unstated—Writers on Scottish Independence*. He was a founder member of the Edinburgh RIC group, the first in Scotland.

The UK—My Part in its Downfall

For more than forty years prior to Indyref 1, I had been involved in a number of inspiring struggles. These seem to suggest that another Scotland and another world are both possible.

The first of these was the large-scale independent (unofficial) strike action by Scottish teachers in 1974-5. This was led mainly by the post-1968 generation straight out of college, very much influenced by the heady politics of the time. I was an activist in Scottish Rank & File Teachers (SRFT) and the East of Scotland Action Committee. These organisations were to the forefront of the action in Edinburgh, the Lothians and beyond. We didn't overturn the educational order, but for about 17 years we changed it for the better. The Educational Institute of Scotland was transformed from a conservative professional association into an active trade union. Several of those I worked with in SRFT from 1972 have remained my closest friends to this day.

A decade later, in 1984-5, I was involved in the Edinburgh Miners' Support Committee. After four years of Thatcherism, the miners' strike offered hope and inspiration. There was widespread solidarity, including from beyond the UK. I joined the picket lines and miners' support marches. I helped to organise weekly collections in the schools. I joined fellow teacher, the late Jane Colkett, in taking this money every week to the welcoming Gilmerton Miners Welfare Club. Some of my school colleagues also organised a very successful disco there. Again, I made new friends and comrades. I am still close to several of these people today. But sadly, the miners we were most involved with had to take other jobs (or they retired) and these contacts based on the solidarity of the strike were lost.

In 1988 I became Chair of the Edinburgh and Lothian Anti-Poll Tax Union, the first such city and region-wide organisation in the UK. The campaign was based on an extensive network of local anti-poll tax groups. They met monthly to discuss strategy and tactics. We became a part of the Scottish Anti-Poll Tax Federation (SAPTF). A campaign of non-registration was followed by a massive campaign of non-payment in defiance of Thatcher's Tories and Scotland's Labour councils. These actions were supplemented by the occupations of council chambers, sheriff officers' premises and peoples' homes threatened with poindings. In the process, I made new friends and comrades who have remained close to this day.

With the Tories testing out the poll tax in Scotland a year before anywhere else, the SAPTF pioneered a strategy of 'internationalism from below'. The campaign was taken to communities in England and Wales. The defeat for Thatcher provided a whole new impetus to politics in Scotland. It would eventually contribute to a new Scottish internationalism on the Left, no longer dependent on the UK state, the Labour Party or trade union officials while also being sceptical about the constitutional nationalist SNP wedded to neo-liberalism. The first seeds of a new socialist republican politics, which encouraged people to reject being passive British subjects and become active Scottish citizens, developed out of the anti-poll tax struggle.

By the time Scotland's independence referendum campaign was announced in early 2012, the majority of the Left in Scotland had come to support Scottish independence. In some cases, this was a very recent 'Damascus road' conversion. They could now justify support on the grounds that the Indyref 1 campaign was really a surrogate anti-austerity, anti-Tory campaign. Such supporters, though, downplayed the democratic issue of Scottish self-determination and how this could be exercised.

Despite some of the post-2006 divisions amongst the Scottish Left following the fallout from the Tommy Sheridan affair, the new Radical Independence Campaign (RIC), announced in June 2012, was able to unite the overwhelming majority. This was shown by RIC's three annual conferences in 2012-14, attended by 800, 1200 and 3,000, respectively.

I threw myself into this campaign from the start. Once again, Edinburgh, partly building on its own distinctive campaigning legacy, was to the forefront of this. Edinburgh RIC was the first local group in Scotland. Since early 2013, we have maintained continuous activities, discussions and debates. These have also been archived.

The sheer scale and scope of the Indyref 1 campaign was unprecedented. Had the campaign remained in official SNP 'Yes Scotland' hands, it is unlikely that it would have pushed support for independence from beyond 28-33% initially shown in opinion polls to the 40% which could make Scottish independence a mainstream issue. This is what was to challenge the extremely conservative UK state, steeped in its imperial, unionist and monarchist legacy.

The October 2012 SNP conference highlighted the kind of campaign that Alex Salmond and the SNP leaders were preparing. They did not intend to challenge much of the existing socio-economic and political order. They wanted a saltire-flagged managerial buy-out of the Scottish assets of UK plc. And to signal publicly their 'safe pair of hands' approach, SNP leaders also publicly choreographed a ditching of the party's longstanding opposition to NATO. These leaders included prominent MSPs, both on the Right and 'Left' (e.g. Kenny MacAskill and Alex Neill) of the party.

However, the opposition at the SNP conference was much greater than the leadership had anticipated. This led to the resignation of two SNP MSPs and many local activists. It also contributed to the large attendance at the RIC conference a month later. Although the official national 'Yes Scotland' campaign was always kept strictly under the control of SNP apparatchiks, many local 'Yes' groups maintained their autonomy. These were supplemented by, among others, Women for Independence, Scottish Pensioners for Independence, Scots Asians for 'Yes,' Africans for an Independent Scotland and English Scots for Yes.

Several local 'Yes' groups worked closely with Edinburgh RIC. These included Edinburgh North and Leith, which largely left registration and canvassing in the schemes of Pilton and Muirhouse to RIC. We also worked with the more grassroots 'Leith Says Aye,' which organised regular street campaigning and canvassing. Iain Simpson, a key Edinburgh and Leith RIC activist, devoted much of his time to the campaign in Leith. We worked with the Yes Craigmillar and Niddrie and the closely associated Trade Unionists for Independence. They operated out of the White House on Niddrie Mains Road and the Jewel Miners Club. Derek Durkin was a key figure in this.

I was involved in canvassing and registering in the housing schemes of Muirhouse, Craigmillar, Niddrie, Bingham and Southhouse. The registration of potential young voters outside Craigroyston Community High School was one of several RIC activities filmed by Joel Venet of Screen Education Edinburgh. On another occasion in Muirhouse, young African-Scottish children were keen to be photographed alongside the Edinburgh RIC banner. The conversations and arguments on the doorsteps, along with the invites for tea and biscuits, were particularly encouraging. One day when Edinburgh RIC Secretary Pat Smith and I were canvassing in Bingham, we accidentally triggered a lively street debate. This was focused on two Romanian brothers, one arguing against and one arguing for Scottish independence.

And it wasn't just registering voters, canvassing, meetings, or street stalls. This movement also drew on a tradition of oppositional Scottish arts and culture, going back to the late 1950s and 60s. This had burst forth again in the dark political days after the defeat of the 1979 Devolution Referendum. In order to bypass the largely conservative and upper class dominated cultural institutions of the UK state, Scottish artists and performers involved in the ongoing cultural renaissance made their own international connections. During Indyref 1, the BBC fell back on its UK state-supporting role signified by the first letter of its name—British. The National Collective (Imagine a Better Scotland) provided a challenge to this. This included their month-long 'Yestival' tour of Scotland.

However, as well as many well-known performers who supported the national 'Yes' campaign, local groups produced their own street artists. In Craigmillar, Ryan Randall, the pyro-piper, with his bagpipes spouting flames, became an imaginative feature of the local campaign. On 18 September 2014, he led many who had never voted before to the polling station in the local library. Edinburgh RIC had radical folksingers, Eileen Penman and Gerry Mulvenna, who performed at different events. Edinburgh RIC and 'Yes' groups were able to draw on the photographic skills of Craig Maclean, a socialist veteran of the anti-poll tax days.

Although Craigmillar had lost its pioneering Festival Society, the tradition of local community cultural promotion and support continued and enhanced the local 'Yes' campaign. Similar support came from other community-based organisations. More recent than Craigmillar, is the Muirhouse Millennium Centre. Willie Black had a long history of organising with the community in Muirhouse. The Adult Learning Project, based in Tollcross Community Centre, also provided support. Several people, including Dave Hewitt, were involved.

The Out of the Blue Drill Hall (OOTB) in Leith, initiated by Rob Hoon, with the backing of his partner Julie Smith (both veterans of the anti-poll tax campaign), was an important centre during the Indyref 1 campaign. OOTB is not just a local community centre but has supported many radical causes in Edinburgh. These included the annual Radical Book Fair, organised by another strong supporter of an emancipatory Scottish independence, Word Power Books.

Word Power was run by Elaine Henry and Tarlochan Gata-Aura. They published *Unstated—Writers on Scottish Independence*, to which I made a contribution. However, Tarlochan's involvement went further. He was keen to provide a forum for a specifically socialist republican rather than a Left social democratic approach to Scottish independence. The Word Power online forum provided me with one opportunity to do this, in the aftermath of the first RIC conference.

This followed Mike Small, giving me the space to advocate a republican strategy for Scottish independence in *Bella Caledonia* before the first RIC conference in 2012. I became a regular contributor and have continued to provide articles about RIC and the wider independence movement. Significantly, *Bella Caledonia—'Fresh thinking for the New Republic'*—was first announced at Word Power's Radical Book Fair in 2007. Bella Caledonia was co-founded by Kevin Williamson, one of the drafters of the social republican Declaration of Calton Hill, which was launched at the rally on that site on 9 October 2014. Today Kevin works with Neu Reekie! which is a significant Scottish internationalist literary and arts production house.

But Edinburgh has much older radical roots. Ray Burnett, an RIC member and Edinburgh exile now living in Benbecula, has outlined Edinburgh's subversive radical history. This goes back to the 1790s, re-emerging at various points in the nineteenth century and giving rise to James Connolly, born in the Cowgate. He is probably the greatest socialist to have emerged anywhere in these islands. He enjoyed close links with suffragettes, republicans and socialists, e.g. Winifred Carney, Constance Markievicz, Sylvia Pankhurst, and Margaret Skinnider.

Connolly's memory was opposed by the UK state, the Scottish judiciary, the local police and Edinburgh City Council, as well as by loyalists and other fascists. In 1986, during the period when the City Council was briefly of a Left Labour complexion (1984-6), Helen Clark, Keeper of Social History, organised the *Sing a Rebel Song* exhibition in the City Arts Centre. This was attacked by loyalists. But in 1986, the James Connolly Society (JCS) took to the city's streets to challenge a ban on marches and to defy the loyalists. The JCS won increasing support and success. In 1992, Jim Slaven stood as JCS candidate for the City Council. He was the first person, since John Maclean in Glasgow in 1923 to stand on a Scottish Workers Republican platform. When it came to the Indyref 1 campaign Jim spoke for the JCS at an Edinburgh RIC meeting, which also had a Catalan speaker. Three Edinburgh RIC speakers, Andy Ashe, Liam O'Hare and myself, spoke at different events organised by the JCS.

However, RIC's Irish connections stretched beyond the city. I spoke for RIC in Dublin and Belfast, being joined in Belfast by Tommy McKearney, former hunger striker and now organiser for the Independent Workers' Union. And I also had the great pleasure of speaking alongside Bernadette McAliskey at the 'London Says Yes' rally on 6 September 2014. However, Edinburgh RIC's internationalism can be seen as early as our second posting. Alice Bowman spoke at the ALP sponsored Spanish Civil War Memorial Event in Tollcross Community Centre. During the Indyref 1 campaign, Edinburgh RIC organised solidarity meetings and attended demonstrations in support of asylum seekers, migrant workers and Palestinians.

Two events organised on 17 September 2014, the eve of the referendum, represented the culmination of our local and international work. A packed public meeting in the Augustine Church on George IV Bridge, chaired by Pat Smith, was addressed by speakers who included Lesley Riddoch, Gerry Hassan, Jordi from Catalunya and Alister Black (Edinburgh RIC). But we also organised an international rally on the Meadows, one of the venues used by James Connolly. There were 1500 people there with flags from all over the world, including an official representative from Papua New Guinea who had come to observe the referendum count. I attended the rally with a group of Welsh republicans who had travelled north to work for the 'Yes' campaign in its last week. I had written the Edinburgh RIC address for the 'Go For It' rally in Cardiff on 6 September. The lead RIC speaker on the Meadows was young Amie Robertson. She announced an impromptu march, which was joined by those from the Augustine Hall, and many others as it proceeded down the High Street, finishing at the Scottish Parliament.

For Edinburgh RIC, just campaigning for a 'Yes' vote was not seen to be enough. We had been involved in supporting many economic and social struggles and provided international solidarity. We were aware of the radical history and traditions of our city. We put forward a key proposition at the 17 May RIC national assembly in Glasgow. In the event of a 'Yes' vote, we called for the RIC national conference to become an organising centre for all the autonomous 'Yes' groups. This conference would recognise the republican principle of the sovereignty of the people and begin to organise Scotland-wide peoples' assemblies in preparation for a Constituent Assembly. This proposition was overwhelmingly agreed.

My hope had been that the 'Yes' vote would reach well above 40%. For a brief period in those heady last few days, I even thought that a very slim 'yes' majority might be achieved. When the result was announced the next day, there was initially widespread disappointment. We had organised a post-referendum RIC meeting in a room in the Edinburgh Central Library, not expecting too many in the circumstances. One young chair for the evening, Stuart Roger, had to announce a move to an open-air meeting back on the Meadows attended by 136 people. Some 3,000 were to attend the RIC conference in Glasgow *after* the referendum vote.

We soon realised we had been part of a democratic revolution in which 95% had registered to vote, and 85% did actually vote—something unprecedented in UK politics. For the British ruling class, it was a pyrrhic victory. The issue of Scottish independence had become mainstreamed, and the continued existence of the UK state looked increasingly doubtful.

Liz MacRae Shaw

has her grandparents to thank for her love of Highland music and culture. Her grandfather, Seonaidh Bán (Fair John) was a fisherman all his life on the Isle of Skye. It's an occupation that is sometimes romanticised but which in reality is physically challenging and dangerous as well as being economically uncertain. Her granny Dolina, like many young Hebridean women, had to leave home for work and she travelled to Glasgow to work as a nursery maid for a wealthy family. They were both born in the Bayfield area of Portree, by the sea among other fisherfolk. The Second World War and the dislocation it caused meant that their children moved away, but Liz and the other grandchildren all felt the pull of the island and came back regularly for holidays. Liz considers herself fortunate to live now on Skye. Her novels include *No Safe Anchorage*, *Had We Never Loved So Blindly* and her historical novel *Love and Music Will Endure*, based on the life and times of Máiri Mhòr. http://www.lizmacraeshaw.com

Màiri Mhòr nan Orain

Gaels have always loved nicknames. Mary McPherson earned her title of 'Great Mary of the Songs' because of her achievements as a bard and political campaigner during the Land Wars of the nineteenth century. Angered by the plight of her fellow Highlanders who were being driven from their homes, she overcame the barriers of background, class and gender to become their champion and inspiration.

I first heard of her from my Granny who lived on Skye all her life and maintained that Màiri was in our family tree. Sadly, I have found no evidence of this, although it is possible that the connection is through her husband Isaac.

The outline of her life is well established. Professor Donald Meek's collection of her songs includes a biography written in Gaelic, which is the only detailed account of her life since McBain's brief biography, written in 1891 to accompany the publication of her songs. However, despite her living in the modern age, there is ambiguity about her date and place of birth. Accounts of her age at her death in 1898 vary but her tombstone records that she died at the age of 80. Arguably, a variation of a few years is not very significant and there are also differing accounts about her early childhood.

There is some doubt about her place of birth in North Skye. It is known that her parents, Iain and Flora MacDonald, lived in Skeabost in 1841 because that was the year that her father built a well there. However, there is nothing left of the original township so there can be no certainty about her precise birthplace and Uig has also been suggested as a possibility. MacBain writes that her parents planned to emigrate in the lean early years of the 19th century. In preparation they sold their cattle before leaving for Glasgow, but the family did not emigrate as planned because they had been told lies about the land available to them in Canada. Instead, they stayed in Glasgow for a dozen years before returning to Skye. All their children were born in the city, except for Màiri and her brother, who were born on the island. Oral tradition contradicts some of this account, claiming that she was eight years old before she returned to Skye.

Her songs resonate with the beauty of the natural landscape of the island. She describes the sun rising on the slopes of the Old Man of Storr and driving away the darkness while the lark sings high above. She refers to celebrations, wintertime weddings, and ceilidhs where the only lantern was a burning peat. She also describes the preparations for winter at Martinmas, a time for making heather ropes and rush bags, of preparing barrels of potatoes and salted meat.

There is no documentary evidence of her childhood and early adult life. She had no formal education, and while her community had a vibrant oral culture, it was not a literate one. MacBain writes:

> Mary spent her youth and early womanhood... in acquiring ample experience in the management of cattle and all that pertains to the conduct of a house in the olden days, from cooking to cloth making and further, in storing her mind with the lays and lyrics of her native isle.

Records show that she was married in Inverness in 1847 but it is not known when she moved there. The timing is critical because if she left Skye before 1845 she would not have had personal experience of the devastating effects of the potato famine which struck there in 1846. She tells us that she was in Inverness in 1845, twenty-seven years before what she refers to as *an tamailt* (the disgrace) that befell her in 1872.

Her marriage in 1847 to Isaac MacPherson, son of a hemp weaver, is the first time when her name appears in any sort of official record. Her husband's occupation is recorded as that of a shoemaker or cobbler. The couple are recorded in the 1861 census as living at 3 Wright's Lane in the Maggot area of the town, near the River Ness. The records of births show that six children were born to them: five daughters and a son. One daughter died young.

Deaths in childhood were common, but that did not make the experience any less painful for the parents. The next tragedy to strike the family was the death of Isaac in June 1871, of acute meningitis, at the age of 55. Màiri became the head of the household and was forced to look for work to support them all. In 1872 she found employment nursing Harriet Eliza Turner, the young wife of Captain Turner, an officer in the Royal Engineers. Mrs Turner was suffering from typhoid and died after two weeks of illness, at the age of 32. Nursing typhoid victims cannot have been a popular job because of the high risk of infection. The fact that Màiri took on this role suggests her desperation to provide for her family at all costs. She certainly paid a high price for this work.

The *Inverness Courier* reported that:

> Mary MacDonald or MacPherson was engaged to attend a lady lying ill of fever. The lady, comparatively a stranger in Inverness and living with her family in lodgings unhappily died and the nurse took advantage of her position to pillage her wardrobe. While the funeral service was being read at the Cathedral she was ransacking the boxes of her deceased mistress. The charge was fully proved and the prisoner sentenced to 40 days imprisonment.

Màiri's distress and rage at her sentence led to an outpouring of songs. She linked her own experience of injustice in a court where she was unable fully to understand the proceedings with the harsh treatment of her fellow Gaels who were being evicted from their crofts. She always maintained her innocence, but does the evidence support her?

William Mackenzie, *Old Skye Tales, Traditions and Memories*, 1995, wrote about an oral tradition that there was another servant in the house, a Lowlander who took a dislike to Màiri and set about incriminating her. Màiri herself said nothing about this. She believed that the court was unduly influenced by Baillie Simpson, who presided over the case and had a history of animosity towards her husband, Isaac. The question of her guilt or innocence cannot be resolved because the relevant police accounts have been lost. Professor Meek believes that she was innocent and I agree with him. It is difficult to believe that a guilty woman would have protested her innocence so vehemently. Also, at that time false accusations against servants for stealing clothes were all too common.

Unsurprisingly, Màiri had no wish to stay in Inverness. With the encouragement of the lawyer, Charles Fraser Mackintosh, and John Murdoch, owner of *The Highlander* newspaper, she moved to Glasgow with her younger children and embarked on a new life, training as a nurse and midwife at the Royal Hospital. To achieve this, she would have needed to become fluent in English as well as learning to read and write the language in order to pass her examinations. This was a considerable achievement for a woman in late middle age. In 1876 she moved to Greenock where she continued with her nursing career but travelled back frequently to Glasgow to sing at ceilidhs.

'*She found a very lively Skye community... where she was feted as what we would now call a 'celeb'*', said Fiona Mackenzie, Màiri Mhòr fellow. As well as the social aspect of these meetings, she would have heard discussions about the issue of land reform and crofters' rights. It was unusual for a woman to appear on stage at political meetings, and Màiri experienced her share of hecklers. She was able to stand her ground, as was shown by one of the famous anecdotes about her. Morag Henrikson recounts the story told by Simon MacKenzie from the island of Harris. Màiri, as usual, was singing the praises of Skye when a man called out, 'What use is Skye? You've got nothing there but rocks and nothing to eat but potatoes.'

Màiri was not put off by the heckler. Instead, she turned her back, raised her skirts and slapped her considerable rump and shouted, *'Seall an da bhannachan a chuiur an t-eilean Sgitheanach agamsa!'* (*'Look at the two bannocks the Isle of Skye gave me!'*).

Màiri was longing to return to Skye, and she was given help from a surprising source—a wealthy landlord, Lachlan MacDonald. He was the archetypal younger son who had travelled abroad to make his fortune. He became an indigo and tea planter in India, returning home a wealthy man and bought the Skeabost and Bernisdale estate. He was an unusual landowner for the time, being a fluent Gaelic speaker who encouraged Highland culture. He listened to the concerns of his tenants and invited them to suggest what would be a fair rent for their holdings. This was revolutionary at a time when so many landlords imposed extortionate rents and had no compunction about evicting those who could not pay. His granddaughter, Felicia, nicknamed Wytchy, tells of how Lachlan was the only landlord on Skye who could venture out in an open pony and trap during the 1880s, a very revealing remark. Other landlords presumably ran the gauntlet of clods of earth, or worse, being thrown at them. Lachlan gave her a cottage to live in rent free, *Bothan Ceann na Coille* (*Wood End Cottage*). It is still there today. Lachlan paid for the publication in 1891 of her writings, *Dain agus Oran* (*Poems and Songs*).

She returned home during the time when Skye was at the epicentre of the Land Wars. In 1882 a dispute between Lord MacDonald and his tenants in the Braes, a collection of crofting townships 8 miles from the island's capital of Portree, finally boiled over. The neighbouring hill, Ben Lee, which could carry over 1,000 sheep, was traditionally common pasture land for the villages until Lord MacDonald leased it to a sheep farmer, denying the crofters access to it. The success of the Irish Land League in contesting similar issues over the sea inspired the Braes crofters to stage a rent strike. An attempt to serve eviction orders on the leaders of the strike led to a large crowd seizing the sheriff-officer and burning his summonses. William Ivory, Sheriff of Invernessshire, marched from Portree with a force of 50 Glasgow policemen to arrest the leaders. They were successful in this but on the way back were surrounded by local people, many of them women, as they reached *An Cumhang*, where the narrow road crossed a hillside rising sheer from the sea. Some of the crowd were injured, including 7 women.

The policemen kept hold of their captives who were later tried in Inverness Sheriff Court rather than at Portree where local opinion supported the accused. Within a few days, no fewer than 11 journalists from national papers descended on the island. Their descriptions of the poverty endured by the local population swung public opinion in their favour.

Màiri herself was not at the Battle of the Braes. As a big, powerful woman, she would probably have been ready to take on the police. However, she composed a song, and when the leaders were released from prison, she travelled down to the railway terminus at Strome Ferry to greet them:

'S na mnathan bu shuairce
'S bu mhodhaile gluasad
Chaidh an claiginn a spuiceadh
Ann am bruachan Beinn Li.
(The women, gentle, graceful
Skulls split open on that hillside
By the braes of Ben Li).

As well as championing land reform through her songs, she travelled widely campaigning on Skye, the other Hebridean islands and the mainland. She joined Fraser Mackintosh on his steam yacht for the election campaign of 1885. She was a huge asset at these meetings as she could communicate directly with the audience and with humour, in their own language compared with the more staid, middle-class lawyer. The campaigning was successful as four crofter candidates were elected to Parliament:

> The commercial landlordism introduced into the Highlands in the eighteenth century was at last on the retreat. And for the first time in the nineteenth century, Gaelic poetry took on an optimistic tone—best exemplified in the work of Màiri Mhòr nan Orain, that committed and outspoken land reformer, (James Hunter, The Making of the Crofting Community).

However, there was no humour in her mock elegy on Sheriff Ivory who in 1884 decided to pacify Skye by marching 250 marines around the north of the island. His plan to intimidate the crofters backfired. The display of force excited, *'the astonishment, and mirth even, of the crofters but did not cow them,'* according to a *Times* correspondent.

The tide was turning in favour of tenants' rights and in 1886 the Crofters' Act finally gave security of tenure to crofters and set up the Crofters Commission, which had the power to fix fair rents. Unfortunately, there was little provision for making more land available to crofters. However, the greatest achievement of the Act was to end the situation where landlords could act with impunity against the interests of the crofters.

Màiri's hopes of a new dawn in the Highlands, with the wheel turning so that exiled Gaels returned from overseas, sadly, never materialised. She kept singing until her death in 1898. She spent her last days in what is now the Rosedale Hotel, in a room overlooking Portree harbour. At that time it was a Temperance Hotel, and she aroused criticism from the more religious local people because she kept singing Gaelic songs rather than contemplating the afterlife.

Her life is only just beyond the scope of oral memories and there are many anecdotes about her, for example how she scandalised her neighbours by keeping a pet fox in her house and how she enjoyed watching a shinty match or having a dram or two. Mary Ann MacFarlane of Tote tells the story of how Màiri delivered her aunt. The child's mother was horrified when Màiri told her to bathe the newborn in cold water from the nearby River Tora. She did as instructed and the child grew up never feeling the cold and outliving all seven of her siblings.

Many of the tales about her may well have been embellished, but they resonate with her character. We can picture her travelling around Skye in a horse and cart, visiting people with a basket of bannocks and crowdie on her arm and demanding that her herring be cooked by placing it directly on the peats in the old way.

Lesley Orr

is a historian and activist from Edinburgh, and has worked at the Universities of Edinburgh and Glasgow. Her interests span the histories of feminism, religion and social movements in modern Scotland. She also has extensive education, training and consultancy experience, working with the Scottish Government and women's sector including Rape Crisis and Scottish Women's Aid. Lesley was partner for an AHRC 'Voices of War and Peace' project, working with Glasgow Women's Library on FORWARD! commemorating the centenary of the Women's Peace Crusade. She 'represented' Helen Crawfurd at the 2019-re-enactment of the Zürich Women's International Congress, featured in the film *Versailles 1919: Return of the Dangerous Women*. Publications include 'Shall We Not Speak for Ourselves?', 'Helen Crawfurd, War Resistance and the Women's Peace Crusade 1916-1918', *Scottish Labour History* 50:2015.

Helen Crawfurd (née Jack) 1877-1954

In May 1919, hundreds of leading feminist war resisters from across Europe and beyond gathered in Zürich. The conference, organised by the International Committee of Women for Permanent Peace, met just as the punitive Versailles peace terms had been published. It was a significant occasion for these women from sixteen belligerent and neutral nations, constructive activists for peace in the face of hostility, repression and persecution. The International Congress of Women met in turbulent times to report on these actions, respond to the Peace Treaty, and make plans for the future. At the opening session, Helen Crawfurd from Scotland gave the report of the British delegation. In her unpublished autobiography, Crawfurd recalled the occasion. Naming other prominent delegates involved in leadership of local and national war resistance (including fellow socialists, Ethel Snowden, Charlotte Despard and Margaret Ashton) she commented, *'It was quite remarkable that a comparatively unknown Scottish woman should be given this honour.'*

By 1919, this minister's widow from Glasgow was a battle-scarred veteran of the suffragette campaign, a leading member of the Independent Labour Party, a persuasive orator and prime instigator of the Women's Peace Crusade (WPC)—a grassroots movement of working-class women which was launched in the summer of 1916. In 1917 the WPC spread rapidly across the industrial heartlands of Scotland and beyond to become a mass movement of women against the horrors of a global capitalist war, campaigning for a negotiated 'People's Peace' in the face of hostility and violent intimidation.

Mrs Crawfurd was a bonnie fechter who believed passionately in the need for women to awake from their oppression, to break the imposed silence of centuries, to organise and to claim the right to speak for themselves. By the end of the war she was a key figure, and she should be recognised alongside

Gallacher, Maclean et al., as a Red Clydeside leader, a militant activist at the intersections of popular political radicalism which erupted in and around Glasgow in opposition to the war. In her contributions to debates at the Zürich congress, she argued that the strength of industrial and socialist organisation in Glasgow had made it possible to work more actively for peace there than in other parts of the country.

Crawfurd was also a committed internationalist, and her participation at Zürich helped foster and develop important connections with comrades who shared her revolutionary zeal. In 1920 she made a momentous three-month trip to Bolshevik Russia, securing an interview with Lenin himself. On her return home, having failed to convince the ILP to join the Third International, she joined the newly founded Communist Party of Great Britain (CPGB). From the 1920s she was involved in international workers relief, anti-imperialist and anti-fascist activities, stood as a CPGB candidate in two general elections, and late in life was elected as the first female councillor in the small Argyll town of Dunoon. It was there, in old age and still a loyal member of the CPGB, that she wrote an autobiography, reflecting on her participation in the momentous twentieth century events, causes and politics to which she bore witness.

Helen Jack was born on 9 November 1877 in the Gorbals, Glasgow, the fourth of seven children. Her father was a master baker and trade unionist. Both her parents were active Conservatives and fervently religious. Helen's memoirs describe a warm, loving and hospitable family, brought up with strong humanitarian values. Political and religious issues were discussed regularly and snobbery was discouraged. The family lived in Ipswich during much of Helen's childhood but returned to Glasgow in 1894. The poverty, squalor, slums and ill-health all around shocked her, but Glasgow was also a city alive with street-corner preachers and soapbox orators—including some socialists from whom—'I fled as from the Devil!'

Biblically based evangelical Protestantism was a bedrock of Helen's early life. She became an active member of Anderston Brownfield parish church, and in 1898 the elderly minister, Rev. Alexander Crawfurd, persuaded her that they should marry as part of God's plan for her work of Christian mission. Her life in the manse was a round of Bible study, services and funerals, Mothers' Meetings and prayer meetings. But profoundly influenced by Keir Hardie's series of articles exposing the hypocrisy of Lord Overtoun, who called for the People's Palace to be closed on the Sabbath while demanding Sunday labour and other exploitative practices in his chemical factory, Helen's evangelical fervour was increasingly channelled in political directions, appalled as she was by Glasgow's dreadful social conditions and inequalities:

To me, it seemed all wrong that the religious people should be so much concerned about heaven and a future life, and so little concerned with the present, where God's creatures were living in slums, many of them owned by the Churches, amidst poverty and disease.

The sham and deceit of the respectable religious ruling class was to be a recurring theme in her political formation and activism.

From early childhood, Helen was indignant at injustice—particularly constraints on the lives and opportunities of women. As a voracious reader she brought that critical sensibility to bear on everything she studied, including the Bible. She questioned the authority of injunctions about women:

My husband would say 'Woman, that is blasphemy'... I had always resented any suggestion of the inferiority of women. [Their] status implied by 'let your women keep silence in the churches' made me rebel, but I think it was my respect for women more than this that made me a feminist... I had tremendous faith in women and felt they could do much to change the existing conditions if awakened and organised and permitted to participate in the making of laws.

Political theory, church history, novels, the writings of feminist campaigner Josephine Butler and of Thomas Carlyle were all grist to the mill, as was a love of theatre. Glasgow Repertory Theatre productions of Shaw, Ibsen and Gorky gave potent stimulus to her imagining of a different social order.

It was the suffrage movement which drew Helen into active political engagement. She joined the Woman's Social and Political Union in 1910, quickly becoming a regular speaker for the Cause and a fervent lieutenant to the Pankhursts. She crossed over the line into direct action in 1912, participating in a mass raid in London:

On the Sunday before making up my mind to undertake the job, I went to Church and prayed I would get a message in the sermon. Little did my husband realise what he was doing... His sermon was about Christ making a whip of cords, and chasing money changers out of the temple. This I took as a warrant that my participation in the raid was right. If Christ could be Militant, so could I.

She was imprisoned on several occasions during the suffrage and anti-war struggles, and militancy became a defining feature of her political analysis, self-understanding and practice, as a clear strategy of confrontation and protest. Her belief in the right and necessity of rebellion against a self-serving, duplicitous and sometimes brutal enemy State were commissioned by her active commitment to the struggle for Irish independence.

When war was declared in August 1914, Helen was horrified at what she considered to be cynical capitalist belligerence between imperialist powers, felt deeply betrayed by the Pankhursts' decision to suspend WSPU activities in favour of pro-war patriotic fervour, and was disillusioned with the rapid collapse of international working-class solidarity. She joined the Independent Labour Party (ILP), carrying her leadership qualities and campaigning experience into anti-war and socialist activism on many fronts.

No stranger to public platforms across Scotland and beyond, she developed a well-earned reputation for the power and passion of her oratory:

> I travelled throughout the country exposing the Armament rings, war makers and urging women to revolt against the sacrifice of their sons and the powerful few who despised them.

Her speeches were sometimes reported in local papers and the socialist press, but also recorded by police officers for surveillance purposes under DORA (the Defence of the Realm Act). Their accounts are evidence that she railed against the waste, violence and slaughter of war. She spoke out against the exploitation, hardship and sacrifice of working people, whether in Britain or Germany, and the need for a transformed economic and political order to bring lasting peace with justice. Her critique extended to the militarisation of industry and the impacts of total war on the well-being, rights and liberties of working people at home in Britain, and especially on women.

It is no surprise then that Helen was deeply involved in the 1915 Rent Strike, supporting her ILP comrade Mary Barbour as secretary of the Glasgow Women's Housing Association which coordinated the successful campaign against wartime profiteering of landlords (see article by Catriona Burness). The GWHA personnel and methods were a crucial bridge between working-class women and peace activism. Helen delivered powerful anti-war and socialist speeches at packed tenants and factory gate meetings. Late in 1915, along with her younger ILP friend Agnes Dolan she joined Quaker women in setting up a Glasgow branch of the Women's International League (WIL), in the wake of the Women's Peace Congress held in The Hague that year. Helen respected her more constitutionally minded colleagues in the League, but refused to comply with DORA censorship and wanted to mobilise anti-war agitation by building a mass movement which was dramatic, direct, rooted in the harsh realities of local working-class women's lives. They protested against conscription, food shortages, the oppressive reach of the State into everyday life, and industrial slaughter in the trenches.

A UK-wide alliance of pacifist, religious, labour and women's organisations set up a Peace Negotiations Committee in the spring of 1916, denouncing the moral iniquity and cruelty of the war, and seeking early negotiations for a just and lasting peace settlement. That summer, Helen organised a public meeting with prominent feminist speakers from across Britain to launch a Women's Peace Crusade: an intensive campaign in Glasgow neighbourhoods, using the methods of the rent strike to inform, rouse and rally women in support of an immediate negotiated peace. Twenty open-air meetings were held across the city, and thousands of signatures collected for the national Peace Petition. The 1916 Crusade culminated on Sunday 23 July in a 5,000 strong demonstration on Glasgow Green. It was reported that the rally *was arranged entirely by women, who have been well led by the able and enthusiastic Mrs Helen Crawfurd, who has no leisure hours that are not devoted to furthering the cause of Peace.*

In the summer of 1917, given fresh impetus by the February Revolution in Russia, the Women's Peace Crusade was relaunched. The call to action spread like wildfire, becoming a national mass movement with meetings, marches and demonstrations in cities and industrial centres across Britain, as women rose up and occupied public space to demonstrate against the war. Sylvia Pankhurst, Charlotte Despard and Ethel Snowden took on leadership roles. Speaking at a WPC rally in Birmingham, Crawfurd declared, *'We are going forward whether you kill us or put us in prison. No matter what you do, we mean to make the voice of women heard, and that this ghastly slaughter shall cease.'*

In Glasgow, WPC activity was an integral element to the growing unrest and agitation across the city, and Helen Crawfurd, collaborating with her close friend Willie Gallacher and the Clyde Workers Committee, was a vital link. She had an eye for the spectacular, a taste for confrontation and a propagandist's skill in subverting the dominant pro-war narrative—often deploying biblical stories and injunctions to good purpose.

When Helen was chosen to speak on behalf of the British WIL at the 1919 Zürich Congress, it was due recognition of her immense contribution to local and national war resistance. Her report declared that the real work of WIL was just beginning and emphasised the importance of seizing the revolutionary moment, tackling the economic causes of war and building socialist alliances. Her vision was for a global culture of international proletarian solidarity.

Helen's own commitment to that cause was lifelong. Between the years 1921—33 she was the British secretary for Workers International Relief (WIR)—a Comintern sponsored organisation established by German communist Willi Münzenburg to encourage workers of the world to respond to crises, conflicts and natural disasters by offering moral and material solidarity. Crawfurd edited the British WIR publication and travelled extensively across post-war Europe. She organised support for victims of Russian famine, Japanese earthquake, German post-war devastation, floods in the west of Ireland, and relief for British mining families during the 1926 General Strike. The WIR was suspected of being a Communist 'front' operation, more concerned for propaganda than workers' relief. Crawfurd regularly countered such accusations, claiming that the WIR was for all workers and socialists, and that it was under attack because it was becoming a danger to international capitalism. In 1927 Münzenberg also set up the League Against Imperialism, and Helen attended the opening conference in Brussels, in the company of leading anti-colonialists from Africa, Asia and the USA.

In 1933, she relinquished her WIR role. She was in poor health, worn out by the constant travel and demands of the work, but perhaps also unhappy with the change in Comintern policy from the 'united front' socialist alliance strategy, to a hard-line class against class position. She remained loyal to Moscow, though, and Münzenberg (who was denounced and expelled in 1938) is not mentioned in her autobiography.

Back home, in 1933 Helen became secretary of the Glasgow anti-fascist committee, supported solidarity work with Jews in the city and the Republican cause in the Spanish Civil War. In 1938, on behalf of the Scottish Peace Council, she coordinated the organisation of an international Peace and Empire Congress, held as a counterblast to the imperial propaganda of the Empire Exhibition.

As a communist, her political activism after the turbulent Red Clydeside years was largely out-with the mainstream of British democratic institutions, though she did stand as a CPGB candidate in the 1929 and 1931 General Elections. In retirement she was elected as an Independent to Dunoon Town Council. Until her death, she regularly wrote to the press on local and international affairs, while continuing to chair and speak on platforms. A CPGB comrade recalled *'Her natural eloquence, native humour, real love of people and burning hatred of all forms of oppression combined to make her one of the finest orators in Britain.'*

While her feminist analysis of women's class oppression did not always sit comfortably with her party colleagues, Helen Crawfurd's mission to rouse the spirit of revolt among women burdened by poverty and oppression remained constant. The Women's Peace Crusade enacted that collective spirit, expressed eloquently in Helen's 'Song of the Women'. Here is the final verse:

Women of the world: we greet you,
Sisters all in heartfelt aim.

Speed the hour when we shall meet you,
Heroines of peace acclaim.
Visions of the life we long for—
Full of joy as children's play—
Urge us on and make us strong, for
Our invincible fight today.

Catriona Burness

is a historian whose work with Workers Educational Association (WEA) local history groups led to several co-produced publications such as The Incomplete History of Castlemilk (WEA, 1993). Her doctorate in political history was published as *Strange Associations: The Irish Question and the Making of Scottish Unionism, 1886-1918* (Edinburgh, 2003). She has held post-doctoral fellowships (Edinburgh, St Andrews) and international study awards (Finland, Sweden, New Zealand) and published extensively on her subsequent research interests in women and parliament. Her research on Mary Barbour was done voluntarily as a committee member of the Remember Mary Barbour Association (RMBA). She wishes to acknowledge the research grant from the Lipman-Miliband Trust which enabled archive research visits—and above all—the many people who helped put the iconic statue of Mary Barbour and Rent Strikers at Govan Cross as an inspirational memorial to a working-class heroine.

Mary Barbour

In bringing together 'Working People's Stories from Contemporary Scotland', Culture Matters sought stories of struggle, suffering, solidarity, and hope, and of imagined alternatives for Scotland and the world.

So, no wonder the editors were keen to include an entry on Mary Barbour!

Mary was the epitome of what the fledgling Labour Party stood for —hard-edged determination to change society for the better, striving for social justice, identifying exploitation and campaigning to end it.

Born in Kilbarchan on 20 February 1875, Mary Barbour was the third of seven children, to Jean and James Rough, a carpet weaver. In 1887, the family moved to the village of Elderslie and Mary gained work as a thread twister, eventually becoming a carpet painter.

She married David Barbour in 1896. Although her husband also came from a textile family, he was a journeyman iron turner. Their first child David, born a few months after their marriage, died of meningitis at the age of ten months, a loss likely to have shaped Mary's deep interest in health and housing issues.

David Barbour's employment took them first to Dumbarton and by 1901 to Govan. By 1911 her husband was a shipyard iron turner and they had two sons, James (11 years) and William (6 years).

In Govan Mary Barbour became active in a range of organisations. It seems she first joined the Kinning Park Co-operative Guild. This linked her to a platform campaigning against poverty and with specific policy demands to counter women's poverty such as maternity benefit, education, the vote, and a national minimum wage. At the same time, the Guild offered

95

Mary Barbour statue by Andrew Brown, Glasgow

its members a structured political education. Mary also became involved in the Socialist Sunday School and the Independent Labour Party (ILP):

> In Govan, Mrs Barbour, a typical working-class housewife, became the leader of a movement such as had never been seen before, or since for that matter... Street meetings, back-court meetings, drums, bells, trumpets—every method was used to bring the women out.
>
> (William Gallacher, 1936)

In 1914 housing was clearly Glasgow's greatest social problem and Mary Barbour had become the 'leading woman in Govan' within the newly formed Glasgow Women's Housing Association. As a political campaigner she was already challenging the status quo.

After the First World War started in 1914, thousands of workers flocked to Glasgow to jobs in the shipyards and munitions factories. Property owners calculated they could raise rents for tenement flats. Instead, fury was aroused, and the rent strike was the response. The historian James Smyth has noted that Govan was the initial storm centre and 'remained the major bulwark of the struggle'.

One of the key players in Glasgow's radical politics, Helen Crawfurd, gave a detailed description in her Memoirs of the tactics used during the rent strike:

> The Glasgow Women's Housing Association took up this issue, and in the working class districts, committees were formed, to resist these increases in rents. Cards, oblong in shape, were printed with the words 'RENT STRIKE. WE ARE NOT REMOVING' and placed in the windows of the houses where rent increases were demanded. When the increased rents were refused, the property owners immediately took legal action for the eviction of the tenants.
>
> The women then organised resistance to these evictions in the following way. In the Govan and Partick districts the working class houses were mainly tenements. One woman with a bell would sit in the close, or passage, watching while the other women living in the tenement went on with their household duties. Whenever the Bailiff's Officer appeared to evict a tenant, the woman in the passage immediately rang the bell, and the women came from all parts of the building. Some with flour, if baking, wet clothes, if washing, and other missiles. Usually the Bailiff made off for his life, chased by a mob of angry women.

Mary Barbour was involved in every aspect of activities from organising committees to the physical prevention of evictions and seeing off Sheriff's Officers. Her contemporaries, Helen Crawfurd and Willie Gallacher, highlight her leadership role with Willie Gallacher coining the phrase 'Mary Barbour's Army'.

By November 1915, as many as 20,000 tenants were on rent strike and rent strike activity was spreading beyond Glasgow to other parts of the country.

The decision by a Partick factor to prosecute 18 tenants for non-payment of a rent increase brought the crisis to a head in Glasgow's small debt court on 17 November 1915. Many of those in arrears were shipyard workers, and there were strikes in support and deputations sent to the court. Thousands of women marched with thousands of shipyard and engineering workers in what the Govan Press described as 'remarkable scenes':

> Amid news of imminent intervention, the cases were dismissed. Within a month legislation was in place and the rent strike's place in history was assured. The Increase of Rent and Mortgage Interest (War Restrictions) Act 1915 introduced rent control whereby rents were restricted to their August 1914 level.

Joseph Melling, the author of the most detailed study of the rent strikes, underlines the importance of the way in which the industrial and housing protests combined to challenge the authority of landlords and the state. James Smyth considers that 'it may well have been the most successful example of direct action ever undertaken by the Scottish working-class'. Mary Barbour's involvement in this struggle made her a local hero in Govan and much further afield.

After the rent strike, Mary Barbour campaigned against food shortages and became involved in anti-war movements.

Socialist groupings such as ILP and the Labour and Socialist Alliance campaigned for peace from the day war started right up to the armistice. The war split the suffrage movement with some militant and constitutional suffrage societies suspending campaigning to support the war effort. The Women's International League (WIL) was formed in 1915 to offer a space to anti-war suffragists. The WIL was cross-party and according to Helen Crawfurd, it carried out important propaganda work, 'Mrs Agnes Dollan, Mrs Barbour, Miss Walker, Mrs Ferguson and myself being the local propagandists'.

This group of 'more active spirits' went on to set up the Women's Peace Crusade (WPC) in June 1916. The aim was 'to hold a conference and take greater risks in our literature and propaganda methods'. The 'risks' involved taking an anti-war message out onto the streets and into working-class areas. Most of the neighbourhood meetings were held during the afternoon and often in back courts, making it easy for women to get involved.

Mary Barbour was a regular speaker at WPC rallies and spoke at the May Day rally in 1917. It must have taken courage. WPC meetings were frequently targeted by pro-war opponents and the police had to be brought in to restore order, as outside Glasgow City Chambers in 1917.

However, she seems to have been more restrained in her WPC and other activity than fellow activists, Helen Crawfurd and Agnes Dollan. Alistair Hulett's song *Mrs Barbour's Army* refers to Mary Barbour having been arrested during the rent strike, but this seems to have been poetic licence on his part. I have not found any evidence of Mary Barbour being arrested for any of her wartime political activities whilst it is evident from press reports that Crawfurd and Dollan were arrested several times. And Agnes Dollan and Helen Crawfurd sought this out. Mary Barbour didn't and perhaps was even more formidable in her restraint.

Post-war, she was a natural choice in 1920 as one of the ILP council candidates for the Fairfield ward in Govan.

This was one of the first elections after most women over 30 won the vote and Lloyd George had made the memorable post-war promise of 'Homes for Heroes'.

The *Govan Press* reported Mary Barbour as saying 'she was asking the working class to send her to the Town Council to look after the domestic side of Town Council works' and she outlined what amounted to a household manifesto:

> The working class had perforce to eat much adulterated food but if there had been a Labour administration in the Town Council there would have been less of that food. She advocated a municipal milk supply in order to secure for the working classes a supply of pure milk. The candidate also expressed her intention to press for the abolition of wash-houses and the provision of public wash-houses where the working woman could have the advantage of all modern labour saving devices... She wanted wash-houses provided so that the working-class woman could take the washing out of the house and bring it back ready for putting in a drawer. She also intended to advocate that closes and common stairs be washed daily, but not by the working class mothers but by women sent by the Sanitary Department to do the job. She would also be in favour of setting up child welfare centres where young children could play instead of having to remain in a tenement.

An article that she wrote for the *Govan Pioneer* looked 'to the future, when housekeeping as we know it, with all the little utensils and wasteful methods of lighting and heating, washing and cooking, that at present make the house-mother little more than a household drudge, will be a thing of the past'. Her article concluded:

> The standard must be higher; better housing, and everything that makes life what it should be in the future must come first; the paying for it is the secondary consideration. Lloyd George has advised that you be daring in your demands. I hope the workers will be greatly daring in their demands, not only for better homes, but for a higher standard of living generally.

At the election she and four other women were elected to Glasgow Corporation, the first women elected in the city since the passing of the 1907 act enabling women to be elected as councillors.

Interviewed in the *Govan Press* just a week after being elected, she said that the new women councillors had plenty of work to do, and from now on would be in the Council Chambers every day. She had already found that work was not done at the Council meeting, but in the communities. She was soon on at least eight committees, many relating to housing, child welfare and public health.

A singular measure of the esteem in which she was held was that her neighbours took her turn to wash the stairs to allow her more time for her council duties!

Her practical focus on improving everyday life is also illustrated by the remarkable Govan scenes in 1924 over the arrival of 'Cheap Fish…. Councillor Mrs Barbour's Idea to Prevent Waste':

> From time to time there have been serious complaints about wastage of food in Glasgow, particularly fish. There are generally two sides to a story, and while the fish vendors claimed that the fish allowed to go to waste was small 'sprats' that should never have been taken out of the water and could not be disposed of to traders in the normal manner, Councillor Barbour and others who shared her views thought it a scandal that the ratepayers should have to pay to have food destroyed in the city destructors while many of the citizens could not get enough to eat. She contended that she would find people who would eat such fish, and on Tuesday, to prove her words, she was offered and accepted two boxes of these small fish. The boxes were sent to Govan, and within fifteen minutes they had been entirely disposed of.
>
> On Wednesday Mrs Barbour agreed to buy at 2s each another dozen boxes of the small fish and the Executive of the Housing Association rallied round to help her dispose of the fish. Instead of only twelve boxes, twenty-four were actually sent

to Govan, and there ensued in Langlands Road scenes baffling description. Women flocked to the stances where the fish was being sold, and for three ha'pence received a great bundle that was nominally supposed to weigh two pounds. The entire twenty-four boxes were disposed of, and so far as can be learned, none of the purchasers burked about the smallness of the fish offered. They were perfectly contented with what they had received.

In 1924 Mary Barbour marked other milestones for women in public office when she became both a Bailie and 'the first fully fledged woman magistrate of the City of Glasgow'.

Her support for Glasgow's first birth control clinic was more controversial. This went against the voting record of her Socialist MP colleagues, none of whom had supported the Birth Control Enabling Bill in 1922. The Glasgow Women's Welfare and Advisory Clinic opened in August 1926 at 51 Govan Road to give advice to married women on family planning.

In 1931 Mary Barbour opted to stand down from the council at the age of 56 stating that she felt 'the difficulties ahead required young and strenuous fighters'. The Govan Press reported her farewell address as a councillor which welcomed changes on health matters but continued:

Eleven years ago those who were returned as representing the working class went forward with certain ideals before them, ideals that they could revolutionise the life of the people of the city, both from a health point of view and from a housing point of view. Those years had been to her a disappointment because of the fact that so little had been done.

When she died in 1958 her obituary in the Govan Press said:

There are women in Govan today who think of Mrs Barbour as one of the great leaders of the Labour Movement who truly represented its spirit and purpose, and I am inclined to agree with them... Mrs Barbour has been out of the limelight of public affairs in this city for many years now but there never was a more revered and loved local leader than she was in the heyday of her active life.

She undoubtedly challenged the status quo of her day, taking on landlords and the power of the state in wartime. She wanted not only to change but to revolutionise living conditions.

Her many accomplishments have had a profound effect on the communities she represented, ensuring that her legacy today is as a powerful role model for the people of Glasgow and especially for the women of the city.

And thanks to the community efforts channelled by the fundraising and awareness-raising work of the Remember Mary Barbour Association, there is an iconic monument in honour of her achievements at Govan Cross. The statue shows Mary at the head of a group of rent strikers. It is now held in affection in Govan and further afield and has become a rallying point for ongoing campaigns for social improvement, a fitting tribute to one of the city's most significant figures.

Kate Armstrong

has a farmer and a fisherman, four generations back, in her background. Born in Berkshire, she mainly lived in Edinburgh and Thurso. She came to Dundee in 1969, and spent twenty-eight years teaching in primary schools, one in a newly established council housing scheme, the other in a largely working-class area near the city centre. In the former, most families were employed in 'the Timex' until it closed down. Many children grew up with no working adult at home. Blind Serpent Press published a collection of her poetry and prose in 1993. She has had many poems published in anthologies and journals and she has given poetry translation classes in Belgium. Since retiring she has done voluntary work as treasurer for Dundee Women's Trail, a charity with at least 25 plaques raising the profile of women deserving to be better known. They give talks and lead walks. They can be found at www.dundeewomenstrail.org.uk.

Mary Brooksbank (née Soutar) 1897 1878

'The warld's ill-divided'

Around 1907, dock worker and trade union activist Alexander Soutar moved from Aberdeen to Dundee with his wife Roseann Gillan and five children. He had moved regularly if there seemed to be a better prospect of employment elsewhere. His wife had worked as a fishwife and a domestic servant. They remained in Dundee until the end of their lives. Soutar, however, was not always fully employed there. Nor were the rest of his family.

In the late 19th century, linen manufacturing was superseded by jute as the main textile industry in Dundee, and the docks were busy. There was plenty of demand for jute products, and the new power-looms could meet this. Raw jute had to be treated, cleaned, heckled, and spun before being woven. The 'jute barons' decided that their workforce would be women, cheaper to employ than men and with no tradition of organising. By 1924, 40% of Dundee's working women were in trade unions.

Mary, the eldest child and only daughter, attended St Andrew's School near the city centre. Attendance was compulsory for children aged 5-13, though enforcement of this was intermittent. Many parents kept school-age children at home 'to run messages', which effectively meant to look after younger children or go out to work. The jute spinning and weaving industry was heavily dependent on women and children. Jute-weaving was relatively speaking a prestige occupation; weavers were skilled and wore hats on their way to work in a factory. Shifters, spinners, and winders wore a shawl, were poorly paid and expendable (and knew it) and worked in a mill. When men reached the age of 18, they were paid off from their work rather than being given the extra pay due to their age. The working day was from 6am-6pm, and conditions were noisy, dusty and dangerous. Mary started work as a half-timer, aged 11, was found out and sent home. There was plenty to do there; the priest called in one day and found her mother was out working in the mill, her father out seeking work and Mary at home washing nappies while looking after four young brothers. The priest, she told her mother afterwards, had sworn, using a word he would use in church, but she knew it didn't mean the same this time.

She began work legally as a shifter in the Baltic Mill, changing the bobbins on a spinning frame. Her 12-hour day earned her seven shillings and sixpence a week. 'A richt wee smerter' was the foreman's verdict on her—'a smart cookie', we'd say. The family moved from rented home to home in the city centre, from the Overgate to Blackness Road to Blackscroft. Mary later recalled, 'We lost a beautiful baby brother, aged 2, a victim of diphtheria. No wonder. The overcrowding was atrocious.' Infant mortality was the highest in the country. A 1905 survey of Dundee schoolchildren's health and housing revealed that many children in the inner city were underweight compared with those in less polluted areas, that 7% had heart defects, that 25% of homes had no indoor lavatories. The poor quality, cramped inner-city accommodation was convenient for the many mills and factories. Mary Soutar, born with defective vision which lasted for over a year, was fortunate in her health and energy. Largely self-educated, she borrowed from the public library and read vast amounts.

The world was indeed ill-divided. Jute-barons' and other businessmen's mansions are still to be found within a few miles of the city centre. Some were benefactors, gifting parkland to the city for public recreation in cleaner air. In 1881, following a drive to establish university education in provincial cities throughout the country, University College Dundee was established. To fund this, Mary Ann Baxter of Baxter's textile dynasty had donated £140,000 of the £150,000 needed. Eminent academics came. Biologist and social reformer Patrick Geddes and his incomer colleagues were appalled at the living conditions, the public drunkenness, the many jobless men wandering the streets seeking work. Professor James Ewing formed a Dundee Sanitary Committee which set about investigating and proposing housing improvements including a better sewage system. Among others, they helped form Dundee Social Union, a precursor of today's social work departments though largely run by volunteers. All this developed further education and raised the profile of the city's living conditions, but had no direct impact on the wages of the poor.

It was not until after World War Two that pressure began to eradicate the slums. 1,500 affordable prefabricated houses were built in Dundee. Other new social housing, though less conveniently sited for the mills and with rents too high for the very poorest, still reduced the incidence of diphtheria, meningitis and tuberculosis.

Mary, like most workers, moved from mill to mill. She had spells of unemployment; she cleaned offices, picked fruit. For a short spell she was a domestic servant—her mother hoped it might make her 'genteel', she later told Hamish Henderson of the School of Scottish Studies in a 1968 interview. The experience simply let her see 'the contrast between their homes and ours'. She also confirmed to Henderson that the chorus of 'The Jute Mill Song' was 'the ditty' often sung by mill-workers, and she had later composed the two verses.

Family life was a rich life for Mary. She married a journeyman tailor, Ernest Brooksbank, in 1924. Her mother encouraged her to keep written copies of her work for possible future publication. The mother figure is a common theme; in the poem 'Bless Them All' we read, *'It was jist my mother's habit/tae gae blessin this and that'*. 'The Docker' stresses the hard, hard work involved, but he sees his children fed and his wife contented. The family sang together. Mary had a high, sweet voice and played the violin. Ernest Brooksbank died in 1943. Several poems lament a lost love. 'Ernest 12/10/43—Memories Dear', surely the quietest epitaph ever, lists remembered countryside places through the four seasons, but includes no 'I' or 'you'— oddly enough, their absence, following the title, brings an unknown man and their life together to mind. Other, more personal poems are 'Alone', 'Memories', 'Life' and 'Love and Solitude'. Ernest is said to have told her she should try to write more from her head than her heart; clearly, he took her writing seriously. They had no children.

Around the age of fifty, she gave up work to nurse her sick mother. Ernest's reliable occupation as a tailor had earned her a degree of financial security unusual for her class. After his death she took in her parents and a nephew to live with her. Her father died in 1953, and two of her brothers had died of injuries sustained in World War One. Mary read poetry aloud to her mother during the latter's last illness. In retirement, she joined the local Old Age Pensioner's Association and became its chairperson; a politically active group, they campaigned on many current causes. Her manifesto/ autobiography, *Nae Sae Lang Syne*, was published in 1970 and calls for peace and justice.

Her poems in English are often long, and deal with a range of different topics, the persistence of war and capitalism being regular themes. There are poems to Thomas Paine, Shelley, Lewis Grassic Gibbon, Lenin. The poem to Stalin is in Scots. Some retain the energy and individuality of her mill poems; others bring to mind Ernest's call for more head and less heart. In 'Forward', she questions traditional religion's account of our status as humans: *'You whose claim is, you're the image of God/ was this all he created you for?'* The challenge also recurs in Joe Corrie's 'The Image o God', the only use I've found in the vernacular. Corrie was Brooksbank's contemporary in

Fife, a poet, dramatist and coal miner: *'Me, made efter the image o God?/ Jings, but its laughable tae!'*

'I have never had any personal ambitions. I have but one: to make my contribution to destroy the capitalist system.' In 1920, having renounced her Catholicism and declared herself an atheist, she joined the Communist Party. Party candidates regularly came bottom of the poll in elections in 1920s Dundee, though with respectable figures ranging from 5,000 to 10,000. Mary organised lobbies and demonstrations for unemployment benefits. She worked in Glasgow for a short period, attending the later public meetings of 'Red' John Maclean, the Glasgow-based Marxist activist who coined the term 'the underclass'. A revolutionary socialist, nationalist and anti-war protester, Maclean campaigned for workers' rights and against Glasgow's housing conditions. Mary led local Party campaigns in Dundee, representing unemployed people at Labour Exchange tribunals, and resisting the eviction of defaulters. Some women Communist Party members visited Russia and came home with unfavourable reports. In 1933 the Party expelled Mary for speaking disparagingly of Stalin.

The drivers of her life were protest, poetry, music and family. Aged 14, she joined a walkout protest among the mill girls, when invited to 'follow the lassie with the green felt hat'. They won a 15% rise. Later she was part of a deputation of the National Unemployed Workers' Committee to Winston Churchill, Liberal MP for Dundee 1908-1922; though a friendly enough meeting, it achieved nothing. Nonetheless, in the 1930s poor relief rose to an all-time high; unemployment soared, with short-time working and workplace conflict common. In 1931 mounted police baton-charged a rally at which Mary was a speaker. She was arrested and charged with incitement to riot, and spent forty days in Perth Prison. Seven days was her penalty for breaking, with others, into a council meeting. The third, also in Perth, was three months for disorderly conduct; the local Railway Women's Guild brought in her meals. In this third term, the prison governor was tasked with observing her to judge if she were sane. He found her sane and loaned her a book about women active in politics. She began to write poetry.

She stormed and led the 300-strong Dundee Working Women's Guild to lobby for better social and health services. She campaigned equally for men and women; she excelled at getting women out to demonstrate. Another cause Mary promoted was the widespread protest against the hated Means Test, a measure so aggressively implemented that 'you could be disqualified for having a paper round'. If you were deemed truly needy, you were given goods, not money. Your home was examined in minute detail and if you had one bit of coal in the house, you could be given no coal.

Music was always part of her life. There was singing in the mills— they lip read, and knew when not to sing. She sang and played the violin; one of her nephews played the accordion. The Soutar family held frequent sing-songs. On one occasion, when there was no money in the house, Mary took the ferry to Tayport and sang in the streets. She made 32 shillings from this, enough to pay the family's rent for just over three weeks.

In the 1950s, folk singer Ewan MacColl performed in a concert at the Caird Hall and said that he wished there were more folk songs from Dundee. Mary Brooksbank felt encouraged to contact him and send examples of her songs and poems. MacColl kept her folder of writing for almost ten years, but did publicise her songs. *Sidlaw Breezes*, her first and only volume of poetry, was self-published in 1966, and sold out. Soon much better known locally and across Scotland, she sang and played in Dundee Folk Club, in old people's clubs and at music festivals, and also appeared on television and radio.

Her poetic themes are politics, love, patriotism, the horror of war, nature, social justice, mill songs. Of the 100 or so poems in the second edition of *Sidlaw Breezes* around half are in conventional English, many others in her everyday 'oary' language, or in many cases a mixture. She described her poems as 'political, pastoral, philosophical'. For me, the mill songs resonate most; I'd add 'personal' to her description because the content stems so much from her people. I've heard these songs sung by the great Sheena Wellington who has done so much to promote Scottish music. Down Foundry Lane in the city centre people gathered in Mary's time to sew sacks, with the jute nailed to a door, the most desperate means of earning a bare living, five pence for twenty-five—for those who could get no better work or were under age. The poem 'Foondry Lane' was written for her people: two ships approach the port with cargo for the jute mills and there's widespread excitement, among the women, children, men who will work unloading, carters, and the old folk. Her verse dances from group to group in one short stanza, then the upbeat tone segues into realism. But undaunted; again and again she states the need to 'bide contented'.

A hand-written copy of her song, 'A Dundee Lassie', shows an untidy but legible cursive script and is written in the same Dundee Scots which can still be heard in the city. An undated photograph of Mary in her later years shows a short, rounded figure with a warm smile and a fresh complexion. Another shows her with her violin and an even wider smile. Her last days were spent with her orphaned nephew in a prefab in the east end of the city. She loved that small house. It had a kitchen and a bathroom and two bedrooms.

The Beveridge Report of 1942 with its 'protection as of right from the cradle to the grave' appeared around the time of Mary's retirement from work. Its identification of the five giant evils: want (poverty), ignorance (lack of education), squalor (poor housing), idleness (unemployment) and disease was revolutionary and its recommendations accepted. All those marches, songs, imprisonments, struggles, protests, after all those years.

Foundry Lane has no traces now of the tiny house which was Mary's home after marriage, and one might struggle to imagine this small woman, five feet tall, walking or working there. The narrow cobbled street divides between the back premises of a retail park and two blocks of attractive modern flats. On the wall of a former jute mill in nearby Weavers Yard, now nicely converted to apartments and managed by a housing association, a plaque (ACTIVIST & MUSICIAN) celebrates Mary's remarkable life. The Brooksbank community centre can be found in Pitairlie Road, Mid Craigie. The last verse of 'The Jute Mill Song' appears carved on the Canongate wall of the Scottish Parliament building. The song is still sung:

> Oh dear me, the warld's ill-divided
> Them as works the hardest are aye the least provided.
> But I must bide contented, dark days and fine—
> There's little pleasure livin affen ten and nine.

Kathryn Metcalfe

was brought up on a council estate in Paisley. Money was in short supply, but books and stories were not. At seven she began to write her own. Her family on her mother's side had a history of political activism in trade unions and workers' rights. In 2012, as part of the Mill Girl Poets, she co-wrote and performed a stage show about the lives of female mill workers. She had been published before online and in print. In 2014 she founded—and still runs—Nights at the Round Table, a monthly event for writers to perform their work in a supportive environment. In 2018 she started a daytime writers' workshop/drop in for local writers unable to attend evening writer groups because of childcare/care responsibilities. She believes that the arts should be more accessible to working-class people, especially those on a low income.

That Was Just The Women

I have a page from the *Paisley Express* tucked into the back of a large family photo album, one of those articles that looks back on local news stories from the past few decades. 'Row over Paisley sex shop', the headline read under a black-and-white photo of mostly women bearing long banners painted with the words JOBS! NOT FILTH! and REFUSE THIS LICENSE.

Above the letters S and E is my mother, holding the end of the banner; apparently, I am there too, just behind her. I had been kept off school because the time of the council meeting conflicted with school finishing, so I was tucked away, invisible.

Mum looks defiantly at the camera. She is one of the younger women at the protest, short auburn hair, long coat, skirt, comfortable shoes. The other women are older, grey-haired, demurely dressed. There were nuns amongst them and some priests, ministers, local councillors, all congregated outside council headquarters in Cotton Street Paisley before the meeting to decide whether or not the sex shop was to be granted a license.

That was 1982. I was six years old during the Thatcher era, living in Glenburn, a large housing scheme in Paisley. Glenburn, a shortbread tin name, made you think of highland villages with stags on the hills and bagpipers striding down through the heather, not a vast post-war housing scheme full of pebbledash, six in a block buildings and cottage types with back and front doors. We lived in a three in a block at the quieter end of our street, on the corner.

It was also the place people stood and talked, especially the men with their banter about football, and who all seemed to be called Jimmy, were red faced, with nicotine-yellowed fingers and lager breath. They always sounded like they were about to start fighting, but that was how they spoke to one another.

Then there were the women, tight jeans over tan tights and stilettos, spiky hair, bleached and dyed, red slashes of lipstick clamped round cigarettes. They swore loudly and cat-called the men. Sometimes they had black eyes after they fought with one another, screaming, grabbing clumps of hair, kicking each other with sharp-toed shoes. I would watch from our window, half terrified, half-fascinated, until Mum pulled me away. They think they're hard as nails, she said, but still fighting over a man. Not worth it.

To me, these women were tough, and I was in awe of them and terrified of them at the same time. They never smiled or seemed to be happy about anything, even though they had trendy clothes, lots of jewellery and were always partying.

The women at Greenham Common seemed happy, though. I watched them on TV, hundreds of them, all singing, holding hands, woollen jumpers and wellies and brightly coloured hats. They were protesting at the nuclear missiles at RAF Greenham down in England. I knew about nuclear bombs and what they could do. It was on the news. Mum and her friends spoke about it. Our kitchen cupboard was full of tins of soup, Fray Bentos pies, sardines, and beans, in case a nuclear bomb went off and we had to go underground.

I began to look forward to seeing the Greenham Common women on the news. I saw their tents, how they gathered round stoves, sang, held placards. It looked exciting. Some of them sounded like Blue Peter presenters. I begged Mum to go there. We could get a tent and stay there and help them, I said. We could take the tins we had, so we had food. Mum shook her head—it wasn't happening. It was too far away and I couldn't stay off school. It was also dangerous.

I was disappointed. In a corner of the living room, I put up a makeshift tent and got my dolls and soft toys together and put on a hat and wellies. I sang songs to myself and pretended to cook things on a stove made out of an old sweetie tin.

It was just Mum and me at home; she didn't work. Before I was born she had two jobs, but now there were few jobs available that coincided with me starting and finishing school. Gran O'Hare worked as a cleaner at different places, so she couldn't look after me during the week. Mum was a devout Catholic, and her life revolved round the chapel. She helped clean it; she read at mass; she was part of its numerous groups. Outside the chapel she was involved in helping out with the local SNP campaigns, and that's how she became involved in the sex shop campaign.

The sex shop. I had no idea what the term meant except that it was something that made grownups very uncomfortable and angry. This sex shop was making a lot of people very angry. At mass the priest was talking about it and calling it a sinful curse on the community. There were meetings in the chapel hall and I sat on the floor and drank Kwenchy Kups and read my Beano while people talked overhead about the threat that it posed to our town, to women, to children.

As children, in school and at home, we were constantly being warned about talking to strangers in case they took us away, like what happened to Susan Maxwell who had been taken away by a bad man. And bad men like that would come to our town and go to this shop and want to do bad things to children after it.

Then I saw it. We were walking down the street and waiting at the traffic lights at the corner when I saw a shop with blacked-out windows. It sat between the bus garage and Lews, the army surplus store on the corner. I pulled Mum's hand.

'What's that in there?' I asked.

'The sex shop,' she said quickly. The traffic stopped, the green man came on and we crossed the road.

'What does it sell?' I asked.

'Dirty pictures!' she snapped, her face white. There was a look on her face that told me not to ask any more questions unless I wanted a slap round the back of my legs.

When the shop opened there were campaigners outside with placards. I knew most of them from chapel; some were my gran's friends too. Old ladies stared down anyone who dared enter the shop. I stood holding Mum's hand while they sang hymns and shouted SHAME ON YOU at anyone who entered or left the shop. Cars passed, horns honking support, which raised a cheer but also shouts and sneers from groups of men in cars, calling out things that made Mum say 'Merciful God' and put her hands over my ears.

At home I watched the Greenham Common women being interviewed on the news, followed by local people being asked about what they thought of them. 'Smelly hippies,' one said. 'They should be at home with a husband and a family, not causing trouble,' another man said.

The campaign continued, with protests, placards, meetings. While I was at school, Mum was down at the shop picketing and would come to collect me. Often she looked as though she had been crying. She said she was fine, then fell asleep on the settee after fish and chips for dinner.

It must have been a school holiday because one day she had to take me with her. Gran couldn't watch me for whatever reason, and there was no one else she knew well enough or trusted to look after me. It was only for a couple of hours, and someone else would come and let her go. She took me to the Lews store, which was where she had worked just before I was born. She spoke to Mr Alec, who ran the shop. I knew him because we always waved and went in to see him when we passed by. He sat me on an old wooden stool and gave me hot sweet tea to drink from a white enamel cup and Jaffa Cakes on a plate. The door was open so I could still see the street. I talked to Mr

Alec, drew in the old ledger he gave me, then went over to the door to have a look. Mr Alec followed in case I ran on to the street.

Mum was standing by the railing with a placard attached to it. She had a clipboard, a petition, and a pen. It was starting to rain, so she put her hood up. Cars went by and splashed her. I could see the marks on her tights. A man shouted at her to go and enjoy herself for a change. Two men walking past tried to push her off the pavement onto the road. Mr Alec swore and told me to go back inside the shop. He lifted an umbrella and ran out into the street. I peeped out and saw him put the umbrella up and hold it over her. He waited until someone came along to let Mum go, then ushered her into the shop to have a cup of tea.

Afterwards, we walked up to the bus stop. I grabbed Mum's hand and wouldn't let go all the way home on the bus and crawled in beside her that night in bed. I was frightened. I didn't want her to stand again in case anyone else tried to push her. I was also getting bored with all the meetings and the constant talk about the sex shop. Gran wasn't happy, either. I told her about the men pushing Mum. She was worried—'You've got the wean to think about, Maureen.' She shook her head and predictably followed with, 'What would your dad say to this?'

Mum just put her cup down and looked at her. 'Dad would say what he always said. If you see something's wrong, do something about it. That's how he brought us up. That's what he did—he spoke up against injustice. If he was here he'd be out, standing at that shop and his voice would be the loudest for it to be shut down!'

'He was a man, though. He didn't have to worry about who looked after you and Dan. It's time to sit down and let the rest of them fight. You have to keep the wean safe.'

'I am keeping the wean safe,' Mum told her, her voice quieter now. 'The other day a bunch of young men went past me laughing and went into the shop. They weren't in there five minutes and they came back and weren't laughing. They asked to sign the petition and while they were all signing it one of them said to me, 'you're right, missis, that place needs to be shut doon. The stuff in there is no right, neither it is.' Then Mum said to Gran, 'It's no Page 3 stuff in there, mammy. There's worse things he's got in there.'

'Kathryn, why don't you go and play in my room, hen,' Gran said.

The day of the council meeting, after the picture was taken, they went into the chamber. I wasn't allowed in. Mum told me to sit in the hallway and she'd check on me. She gave me sweeties and a comic and I sat there swinging my legs and reading quite happily. It was quiet, and there was no one around.

The door at the end of the hall opened, and a man appeared and walked towards the kitchen opposite. He saw me and came towards me. He was an older man and looked a bit like a school janitor.

'You okay, hen?' he asked.

I looked at him and didn't move. The door to the chamber was almost next to me. He smiled and came closer. He looked like someone's grandpa, but I didn't know him. I remembered all the things I'd heard at school.

'Would you like a wee cup of juice?' he asked.

That was it. I was off that chair and through those doors, despite everything Mum said about no children being allowed. She saw me and got to the doorway to stop me from running into the middle of the room.

'Mum, a strange man asked me if I wanted juice and I'm scared he takes me away!' I said. I could see people gathered round the room, the women from the chapel, people in suits, all looking at me and talking in low voices. Mum took me out and closed the door. The man was still there.

'Sorry, missis, I didn't mean to scare the wee yin,' he said.

'It's okay,' Mum said. 'She's been warned not to talk to strangers. Cannae be too careful these days.'

We waited outside the council building to hear what was about to happen. Folk from the chapel and the campaign came out while the council made their decision. Mum had a cigarette while I played hopscotch on the paving stones. I was too busy trying to jump two big square slabs to notice the man coming out to talk to the crowd when a cheer went up.

'We won! We won!' Mum was smiling. She picked me up and cuddled me. 'Praise God!' Then there were people milling about, talking at high volume. I held her hand and hoped that we would be going to the Chinese restaurant for dinner because that's where we always went for special occasions and, though this wasn't a birthday or double money week, this seemed to be a big thing.

I'm ashamed to say that in my teens and twenties I was embarrassed by Mum's involvement in the sex shop campaign. In the subsequent years the campaigners were seen as a bunch of killjoys, frigid even, while I still viewed the women from Greenham Common as radical, more romantic. I went on anti-war protests and claimed the Greenham women as my kindred spirits.

As I grew older, something shifted. I realised that even though Mum and the others wore frumpy clothes and sang hymns, they were every bit as radical as the Greenham Common women; that they faced danger and scorn over their struggle.

Both groups of women were tough, resilient, taking a stand, refusing to give in. And finally, I realised that those women at the street corner, with their spiky hair and unsmiling faces, weren't tough at all. They were scared of Friday nights when their husbands came home punch drunk; that they would lose their jobs before the catalogue debt was paid off; that their kids might be glue sniffing round the back of the local library. Deep down they were as fragile and as afraid of what the future held as everyone else, but were more afraid of letting it show.

Zareen Taj Islam

is a Trustee and former Chair of the Muslim Women's Association of Edinburgh, an organisation that is registered as a Scottish charity. Zareen has worked closely with Tasneem Ali since 2007 to build up their women's group as an anti-war and anti-racist group that also supports Muslim women. In empowering their women through various projects they have also managed to empower families to combat daily Islamophobia and become proud to be both Muslim and Scottish. They can be found at www.mwae.org.uk.

The Muslim Women's Association of Edinburgh

Women of all backgrounds share similar struggles and need the support of their sisters. Since being established in 2005, the Muslim Women's Association of Edinburgh (MWAE) has not only provided that support through the work of our volunteers but extended it to the wider Edinburgh community through our various projects. The unique experience that our work has afforded us has helped unite ordinary people in efforts to fight the racism and bigotry that divides our communities as well as empower women and their families.

Could we ever have thought it possible that a few women dedicated to improving the lives of their sisters could have run so many diverse projects with minimal or no budget at all? The PowerPoint presentation at our AGM held at Muslim Welfare House shows not only slides for the past two years but also the continuing project, 'Love Culture, Hate Racism' (LCHR) that has been a yearly event now from 2013 to 2020. Yes, we managed to get in one more celebration of multiculturalism just before lockdown when other friends from groups that enjoy this celebration also joined our AGM afterwards. As I looked across the hall at the attendees, I felt that I was surrounded by friends: Muslim women and non-Muslim activists from the campaigns that we support. These alliances are not just political; working together means that we inevitably become friends too.

Our main work revolves around women and supporting them through different stages of their lives. In doing this work for our Muslim sisters we have found that we have also provided support for non-Muslim sisters too. Our walks with Greenspace Trust have given us a chance to take friends of MWAE on a canal boat and see parts of Edinburgh they never knew existed. Our toddler group at the Central Mosque has always been open to all and through that we have befriended Scottish grandmas—one of whom has subsequently helped with our mosque garden and another who kindly donated new toddler books for the group.

Through our public events, often held in mosque halls, we have presented meetings and gatherings educating our Muslim and non-Muslim communities on issues as varied as Scottish independence to Climate Chaos. Through the years of demonising Muslims since the time of the Blair government, we have been faced with far-Right protests against Muslims in Edinburgh and the insidious implementation of the Prevent Strategy. Even though we began as a charitable organisation to support Muslim women in their day-to-day lives, we had no choice but to address the negative and damaging stereotyping of Muslims. Women wearing headscarves and travelling on the bus to our toddler group suffered verbal abuse and became frightened of travelling on their own with children. Children coming back from holiday with their families saw their fathers questioned and detained in a humiliating way just because they were Muslim. The clear visibility of Muslim women wearing a headscarf and sometimes an abaya (full length overcoat) made them a target for haters.

These concerns were raised when we met with Justice Secretary, Kenny MacAskill at Edinburgh Central Mosque in November 2009. On hearing the accounts of racial profiling at airports and the disrespectful way Muslim men were treated in front of their families, all the Minister could do was apologise for the conduct of individual police officers who, he said, were 'only human' and so were liable to err or 'have a bad day'. He insisted that when 'bad police conduct' was reported, sanctions would be applied to the offender. However, this disappointing response did not address the central issue of institutional racism or the will to begin implementation of the Islamophobic Prevent Strategy in Scotland.

In an attempt to make people aware of the damage such a strategy would cause to our communities, we held our first Islamophobic conference in 2013. Prevent intended to 'train' civilians to report on other civilians of their suspicion that someone might be becoming radicalised. This is entirely the stuff of Orwell's 'Thought Police' coupled with disinformation about Muslims. MWAE began organising to help dispel the myths and disinformation that led to fear of Muslim neighbours and work colleagues.

We followed up the conference with securing modest council funding for communities and were able to rent St Peter's Church hall for a Saturday afternoon. We aimed to fill the hours with music, poetry, folk dance as well as the very important message on how to fight racism collectively; we Muslim women wearing hijabs were very visible as the organisers and hosts of the event. Our friends from Edinburgh Unite Against Fascism provided a good insight into how we could best oppose racism together with speeches and useful information available on their stall about the positive impact migrants have on our communities and economy. Edinburgh UAF introduced us to Show Racism the Red Card who work very hard to tackle racism and sectarianism among football fans. This has led to talks by footballer Michael Weir at our event and also for our MWAE youth group.

The church hall event was dubbed 'Love Culture, Hate Racism' to link it with the famous 'Love Music, Hate Racism' (LMHR) movement. What occurred to us at MWAE was that LMHR was for adults used to going to gigs but we wanted to provide something that attracted the whole family; what better way to fight racism than to bring up our next generation appreciating world music and culture right here in our city? Such a society may not be visible in a predominantly white Edinburgh, so our event brought choice performers together in one place for all to enjoy. The last three years have even included Book Bug storytelling for the wee ones so no one misses out on the entertainment.

We have often used cultural events to help engage people in issues affecting the people of Palestine. To celebrate the crafts, music, Dabke (Palestinian folk dance) and of course the delicious Palestinian cuisine helps people understand the plight of the Palestinians and give people something positive to experience about Palestine while all around tragic news abounds.

In the same way, in our fight against racism and the damage it perpetrates, we have found that we can create a welcoming environment with our LCHR events. Anyone walking in through the door will be greeted with the warm, aromatic fragrances of Indian and Arabic cuisine and the melodious sounds of the marimba or the foot-tapping beats of African drums. Those who may not be familiar with engaging with people from other cultures in Edinburgh will be able to relax in the friendly atmosphere of folk enjoying poetry, music or dance from Japan or Turkey. Showcasing our local talent in this way is empowering for the youth from our minority communities who can take pride in being different in some ways from their Scottish friends rather than try to hide that difference.

Each year we have had new people attend and got great feedback about the impact of our LCHR celebrations. We do not shy away from the local and world-wide issues so speakers are invited to talk about campaigns affecting us all and most importantly the campaigners are invited to have a stall at our event. Conversations invariably spring up and connections are made that endure for many years to come.

Sharing food and enjoying music together is a fabulous recipe to break the ice and build friendships. Our vision to bring communities together has worked better than we planned. Volunteers have provided valuable help on the day to run the event. The amazing level of professionalism in the acts that perform for us really seals the deal. We feel so lucky that everyone is very happy to contribute to the cause, dispelling myths and smashing the disinformation that proliferates about refugees, migrants and Muslims.

Engaging with other campaign groups has given MWAE volunteers a confidence as we are able to share our experiences and have our voice heard.

We have also learned methods of organising and networking with like-minded people who are pleasantly surprised that Muslim women are doing it for themselves!

The racist groups in Edinburgh are thankfully small but will insist on spreading their hate. One memorable incident was in June 2013 when some parents from a school group pulled out of their visit to the Central Mosque and fed their story to the reporter at the Evening News. We were appalled that headlines read that pupils were withdrawn from the trip to the mosque because parents didn't want their children 'mixed up in hate being preached in mosques'. It was in fact only three parents who had links with the British National Party that refused to send their children on the mosque trip. Rather than speak to anyone at the mosque or MWAE volunteers who conduct the tour, the reporter wrote:

> Kenny MacDonald, Scottish regional organiser of the BNP, backed the parents. He said: 'I applaud these parents in going against the wave of political correctness.'

MWAE got in touch with the reporter and explained how badly his story affected our mosque and community as it perpetrated the myth of hate-preachers radicalising children. The school trip had actually gone ahead, with about 60 pupils and teachers attending. The teachers apologised for the stance of the parents who did not let their children attend such a valuable session where they were able to interact directly with Muslims in their place of worship—in fact, an essential part of the National curriculum. We challenged the reporter to come and attend a mosque tour for himself and learn first-hand about our place of worship.

At one point, the photographer wanted us to go upstairs to the women's area on the balcony so that he could photograph us. We refused, saying men were not allowed there, but women were allowed in the main prayer hall which is for the public, so he had to take his photographs there. Such ordinary information was unknown to the reporter and photographer and they printed a front-page response to the original story correcting disinformation about girls and women being forced to cover themselves when visiting a mosque. It had seemed normal to them to print a story about an intolerant Muslim community and accuse our mosque of 'preaching hate' until we took the reporter to task and gave him a tour of the mosque. MWAE managed to get a positive story about our mosque in print but we hope that we informed the reporter and photographer too about how lazy journalism actually hurts our minority communities.

There have been attacks on our mosque over the years and our wonderful friends from all across Edinburgh have rallied round to hold a vigil of support. These rallies really boosted our community morale and were mentioned in the Friday sermon. Likewise, MWAE called a vigil for the Sikh Gurdwara in Leith after it was firebombed in August 2018. It was important to be sensitive to our Sikh community. They were devastated after the attack and, although no one was hurt, they were unable to use their building until it could be made safe. This gave the Sikh leaders much grief, as they would not be able to host visitors with the normal tea and snacks they love to make for guests. But once they realised that we all really wanted to show our respects at that time of difficulty, the Gurdwara agreed to let us assemble outside for speeches and a show of solidarity. The whole evening was hosted by the Gurdwara committee and broadcast live on Sikh TV across the world. It was wonderful to have instant feedback from viewers in Canada saying they had no idea how well loved the Sikh community was in Edinburgh.

MWAE was proud to have organised the solidarity vigil for the Sikh Gurdwara. We returned almost a year later with Edinburgh UAF for the official re-opening of the Gurdwara, where we presented them with a beautiful framed photograph of the previous year's vigil. We heard several times from the Sikh community how much the support from the vigil meant to them. Such shows of support have also meant a great deal to our Muslim community over the years as we have seen spikes in hate speech and hate crimes. Our children experience a particular type of racism in schools due to them being identified as Muslim: Islamophobia. Such verbal abuse is often considered merely part of normal bullying that does happen in schools and is taken seriously. However, one Muslim woman, Samena Dean, endeavoured to collate information about how widespread such Islamophobia is and to bring information to school communities about what is wrong with Islamophobic attitudes prevailing through playground bullying. Her work has been recognised by those in education and in the Scottish Parliament. We hope that recognising that Islamophobic attitudes exist is the first step to tackling them. MWAE will continue to offer mosque tours, answering visitor's questions appropriately to dispel myths. We will also continue our work to educate our sisters and their families so that we can better counter negative attitudes to Muslims. This vital work joins the work we do to fight racism and bigotry of all kinds.

Carlos Arredondo

is a cultural worker involved in solidarity work since his arrival in Scotland in 1974. For many years he has been working on reconstructing a history of the Chilean solidarity movement. Much of the material used here comes from his own archives gathered throughout the years. He is also a musician and songwriter. He has recorded three albums, the latest one in Mexico last year. He was, for a while, a Unison rep at Stevenson College in Edinburgh. For more information visit www.carlosarredondo.com

A Chilean Testimony of Solidarity in Scotland

It was the time of Salvador Allende, the first democratically elected Marxist-socialist president in the world and an extraordinary period in Chilean history. Politics was at its best, with great debates on the radio, on television, and in newspapers and magazines of all tendencies. There was increased popular participation and a rich and interesting cultural life expressed in filmmaking, theatre, music and mural paintings. Poor children were receiving free milk, and world-class literature began to be accessible at low cost. Allende's was a unique government, paying attention to the needs and future of working-class and rural people, many of whom had until then lived as feudal labourers. This political event attracted admiration and hope around the world as it showed the possibility of choosing, by democratic means, a socialist way of life. Even European statesmen like François Mitterrand visited our country with a French socialist delegation in those days.

However, as soon as Allende was elected president, the powerful establishment parties and their allies in the media became, with the blessing of Richard Nixon, Henry Kissinger, and the CIA, criminally hostile towards the new order. The intention was clear: to propagate fear and destabilise the government at all costs. These relentless reactionary actions continued throughout this period until the coup. Working-class people were, however, resilient in their commitment and support for the socialist cause, increasing Allende's share of the vote as his term in office progressed.

From 1967 to 1973, I worked at Tizona, the biggest guitar factory in Chile. It was here that I learned to play guitar, a skill that, then unknown to me, would prove so useful for my solidarity work in Scotland.

By 1970 I was already very aware of the limitations of our democracy. I wanted meaningful changes to our economic system: deep agrarian reform, nationalisation of the copper mines, reform of our judicial system, which was so clearly on the side of the powerful. As a worker I put all my trust in Allende and the political programme presented to us by Unidad Popular (UP), the left unity coalition he led. Allende was, in my view, a well-respected socialist parliamentarian, a long-standing defender of workers' wellbeing and a proven constitutionalist who respected Chile's settled political traditions, albeit acknowledging they needed deep political and social reform.

At the time, I was involved in the Juventud Obrera Católica (JOC), a catholic workers' group closely linked to the socialistic values of progressive Latin American bishops and priests that formed the base, in 1962-65, for the Second Vatican Council called by John XXIII. The liberation theology movement was the result of this famous council, which had a big impact among working-class catholic communities of our continent.

The coup of 11 September 1973 marked the end of this socialist experiment, the end of Chilean democracy and freedom, and the success of fascism for its allies in the US government. Military and police repression, with civilian and international help, came with astonishing speed and with a force and scale never seen in our country before. Six of my friends from JOC were tortured and murdered. The coup generated international condemnation. Chile became a very dangerous place, so in January 1974 I left for Peru at the kind invitation of the Huapaya-Correa family. I left behind my elderly stepmother, my friends, my work, my story, my barrio and my homeland. It was a very difficult decision to make, as my stepmother depended on me for her maintenance.

I spent six very complicated months in the Peruvian capital. In March, I went to Quito, across the border in Ecuador, to get my visa renewed and a nasty Peruvian consul gave me three days to cross Peru and 'go back to Chile!' I decided to remain clandestinely in his country. By then thousands of my compatriots had also arrived in Peru in desperation. To our relief, the United Nation's High Commissioner for Refugees (UNHCR) came to our aid, opening a special office in Lima. We immediately came under this organisation's protection. They helped us in a variety of ways while we waited for a country to give us asylum. About two weeks after submitting my application to the British Embassy in Lima, I was offered the opportunity to go to the UK. On 18 September 1974 I was among the many Chileans who left Lima for London on a British Airways flight, paid for by the UNHCR. On the plane we were full of contrasting emotions: joy and sadness at the same time. We experienced incredible angst leaving our families behind and our country submerged and defenceless in a bloody dictatorship.

In London we were warmly received in a hotel by the Joint Working Group for Refugees from Latin America (JWG). Composed of people from different parts of the UK, among them Gordon Hutchinson, a very nice Scotsman, the JWG decided that around 35 of us should leave the hotel for Scotland a week after our arrival as rooms had to be vacated to accommodate other Chileans and because there was a committee ready to receive us. Gordon had seen me singing and playing my *Tizona* guitar and kindly persuaded me to come to Scotland. He said that I was going to be well received—'*the Scots love music so you will be happy.*' The JWG was in touch with us regularly and this was very reassuring for me.

Early one morning in October 1974, we left London by coach towards Glasgow and Edinburgh. On the bus there were all kinds of people, including several married couples and a mother with her daughter. We had mixed feelings about leaving London. We arrived on a very rainy night at the home of Mike Gonzalez, his Welsh wife Karen, and their wee children, near the University of Glasgow. A group of about six or seven Chileans continued their journey towards Edinburgh, where there were people waiting for them. We were the first group of Chilean refugees in Scotland. Before us a Chilean had come to Glasgow to continue with his academic work thanks to the good offices of Jimmy Reid, then Rector of Glasgow University.

We were very well received, with food and songs, by a group of academics, students and workers. Among them was Pat, an oil rig worker, who invited me and two other Chileans to a football game at Hampden Park. We were offered accommodation and all the necessary help for the weeks to come. Soon after our arrival, we formed the Circulo Chileno Lautaro in Drumchapel, where many Chilean families lived. Our committee asked me to form a Chilean folk group that was soon in great demand to perform at different solidarity and cultural events in Scotland and England. As many of us did not speak English, music helped our community to connect with different groups involved in the solidarity movement.

In 1978, I moved to Edinburgh. By this point I had already been given the right to remain in the UK. The campaign for Chile in this city was also very strong, with a well organised Chilean community, working hard and closely with the Edinburgh Chile Solidarity Committee (ECSC), the Edinburgh Chile Committee for Human Rights, and the Chile Action Group. The ECSC, for example, constantly engaged councillors and MPs in their local campaign, including John Mackintosh, Gavin Strang, Ronald King Murray, David Owen, Robin Cook, and Ron Brown, of the Labour Party, and Liberal MPs David Steel and Jeremy Thorpe.

Many Chileans took advantage of an academic programme organised by the World University Services (WUS) working in close collaboration with the British Government. At the centre of this programme was the Labour MP, Judith Hart. This programme lasted 12 years, helping about 1,000 Chileans to continue higher education at British universities. Several Chileans came to Scotland, via Argentina thanks to the WUS, and some of them to Edinburgh, with the full support of the group Academics for Chile, headed by Professors Peter Vandome and Martin Pollock from the University of Edinburgh.

I formed another folk group to play at events organised by a variety of organisations in Scotland and England. In 1982, Pope John Paul II came to Bellahouston Park in Glasgow and I was invited by the Scottish Education and

Action for Development (SEAD) to give a short speech about the situation in Chile and to sing a song. It was part of an alternative event within the official programme organised by the Catholic Church in Glasgow. It was an extraordinary experience to speak and sing with my wife in front of 300,000 people!

Philip O'Brien, one of the academics who received us in Glasgow, said that immediately following the coup, a solidarity group, the Glasgow Defence Committee (GDC), was formed at the University of Glasgow. Philip was its Secretary. The committee made contact with the Glasgow Trades Council (GTC) and the STUC, where Jimmy Milne was in charge, who had been first class in his assistance and took a very active role in setting up a wider solidarity movement. At a later stage, the Scottish Chile Defence Committee, functioning through the GTC, was formed.

By the end of October 1973, the Stirlingshire Chilean Action Committee was formed, and in June 1976 it was replaced by the Stirling and District Chile Solidarity Committee with Rowland Sheret as the chairperson. By January 1975, the Solidarity committees in Scotland and the rest of the UK were, along with the Chilean refugees, working closely together. One evening, my Glasgow Chilean Folk Group and some Spanish-speaking members of the GDC went to the Rolls Royce plant at East Kilbride to sing and thank workers who had refused to carry out repairs to warplane engines belonging to the Chilean Air Force. Our intention was to give them moral support and validate the importance of their actions. This event was part of a full week of activities organised in Glasgow by our Chilean committee. On 19 June 1976, we played in Renfrew for a Labour Party event and Michael Foot was one of the guest speakers. On another occasion, we met Tony Benn.

Throughout these years the Scottish artistic community was also very keen to take part in events for Chile: John McGrath's 7:84 Theatre Company, Tom McGrath, The Laggan, The Whistlebinkies, Hamish Imlach, Matt McGinn, Adam McNaughton, Hamish Henderson, Dick Gaughan, The Boys of the Lough, Dolina MacLennan, Liz Lochhead, and Jim Sutherland, among other artists and poets, all made great contributions.

The aim, as in the rest of the UK, was to provide support for the people of Chile against the coup, support the UP and all forces fighting the fascist Junta. It demanded the liberation of all political prisoners, rejection of dictatorship, a break in diplomatic relations, the boycott of all Chilean goods and trade, and a stop to aid and credits. It also engaged in the sponsorship of political prisoners, raising awareness and seeking accountability for disappeared people, assisting Chilean refugees to settle in the UK, writing letters to local newspapers about the situation, involving local politicians in the Solidarity Campaign with Chile at government and municipal levels, and providing moral and economic support to families whose members had been taken prisoner or disappeared.

Below, a campaign newsletter from Cumbernauld and Kilsyth Chile Solidarity in the autumn of 1976, shows some of their solidarity activities:

PRISONER ADOPTIONS. A total of thirteen Chilean political prisoners have been adopted in our area. The adopting groups are Carbrain, Kildrum and Seafar ward Labour parties, the Banton and Queenzieburn branch LP, Cumbernauld Concern, the East Dunbartonshire Liberal Association, a local branch of the EIS, and two Cumbernauld AEU branches. So far, five of the prisoners have been released and effective contact has been established with one of the others.

SEPTEMBER EVENTS

To mark the third 'anniversary' of the fascist coup the Scottish Chile Defence Committee have organised the following: DEMONSTRATION SATURDAY 11 SEPTEMBER

ASSEMBLE Blythswood Square at 11 am. March to Custom House Quay:

Madame Allende, Judith Hart MP, Alex Ferry and Chilean Folk Group

SUNDAY 12 SEPTEMBER

CONCERT: Citizens Theatre, Glasgow 7 pm. Stalls and circle £1.25, balcony 65p

The Laggan, 7:84 theatre group, Phil McColl, Matt McGinn and the Chilean Folk Group are amongst the performers.

CHILEAN PLAY—called Chile 1973 starring Coca Rudolphy at the Edinburgh Festival Fringe, August 30—September 10, Crown Theatre, Hill Place, Edinburgh 5 pm.

Though most of the people involved in the Chilean Solidarity Campaign were Chilean refugees, there were people from other walks of life including academics, workers, trade unionists, the Churches, Amnesty International, the Quakers, human rights groups and members of political groups such as the International Socialists, the International Marxist Group (IMG), the Communist Party and the Labour Party. I hold particular affection for Norman Buchan, a Labour MP and his wife Janey Buchan, a Labour MEP, who helped me personally. In Stirling, Labour MPs such as Denis Canavan, Martin O'Neill and Harry Ewing were great in their commitment. In the words of Dr Douglas Chalmers, from Dundee—'the Society of Friends, the Quakers, the Labour Party, the Trades Council were very useful and... Chileans tended to be housed in the worst areas in Whitfield and in Beechwood.' On Saturday 19 September 1981 a big Scottish conference on Chile and Latin

America was organised at the Caird Hall, Dundee. Among the guest speakers were Hortensia Bussi, Allende's wife, and local leaders like Alec Kitson, then Chair of the Labour Party, and Mick McGahey, leader of the Scottish miners.

The existence of a report in *The Guardian* of 11 September 2013, written by Grace Livingstone, suggested that 'Intelligence officers were sent to infiltrate the Chile Solidarity Campaign.' The British Government was worried that the Chilean Solidarity Campaign was going to ruin the lucrative business of selling arms to Chile, which included submarines and warplanes.

Solidarity with Chile in the UK was not confined to any particular event, individual or political party but was rather a movement. People contributed in different ways to the struggle against the dictatorship and gave solidarity to its victims. I would like to remember the late Andy McEntee, a Scottish lawyer, and for a while Secretary of the London-based Chile Committee for Human Rights. According to *Pinochet in Suburbia*, a drama shown on BBC2 in 2006, Andy played a major role in the detention in 1998 of Augusto Pinochet in London, which had major consequences for our country with deep international repercussions.

It is unforgivable that new generations of refugees escaping from war zones, poverty and natural disasters are not welcome in the UK. Asylum seekers are put in army barracks and horrible detention centres such as Yarl's Wood in England and Dungavel in Scotland. This saddens me profoundly. It seems to me that there is a great contrast between the help and solidarity we received and the hostile environment refugees nowadays face whilst desperately seeking a safe place to settle (and in which to make valuable contributions) in the UK.

Chileans still living in Scotland are very grateful for the solidarity we received and I am glad to report that our own small community, and their children, have made valuable contributions, in different fields, towards the development of Scottish society.

Low Wage by Mark Penrose

Flash Fiction and Short Stories

'...they do less harm than all the faceless corporations that lay our planet waste and trap the poor in drudgery and worse, in the name of profit.'

—A.C. Clarke, 'The Man with the Plastic Cup'

'That's what you do to immigrants, especially people with skin as dark as ours. Have you ever looked at us? Did you see how beautiful my sister was? A rainbow, her friend said, and she was right.'

—Jean Rafferty, 'Didn't She Matter?'

'The wealth of the nation resides in its aesthetic value, and if poverty is ugly, opulence is not to be confused with beauty: the accumulation of capital is not as important to the nation as the accumulation of cultural capital... without cultural independence a country ceases to exist.'

—Cairns Craig, 'The Wealth of the Nation'

Jim Aitken

grew up in Magdalene, a post-war housing scheme in Edinburgh. He taught English at secondary school in the city where he was also the EIS rep. He spent some time as a Multicultural Development Officer producing the first guidelines for the city on anti-racist education. After leaving secondary teaching he has worked with Adult Education and Community Education presenting courses on Scottish History and Culture, Literary Walks and Creative Writing. He has also worked with the Outlook programme for people with mental health issues. He is a writer and poet and has had his work published in a number of anthologies and magazines. Last year he edited *A Kist of Thistles: An Anthology of Radical Poetry from Contemporary Scotland*, published by Culture Matters.

Mrs Lindley and Benny

A full moon revealed her movements that night as she rushed Benny over to the bin and placed her neat bag of rubbish inside and took him on his last walk of the day.

At sixteen and a half years old, he is the fittest dog I know; lean and grey like his owner; wizened and sharp and alert, just like his owner. He is the source of countless talking points in the neighbourhood with everyone she meets; the source of introductions that enable the days to pass. The days go in and the days go round as she walks Benny through the same streets every morning, afternoon and night. Memories often comfort her as she walks, and as she recalls her working life spent as an assistant in various shops and stores.

That night, under the moon, I spotted them both on their last tour of the day. And as they vanished round the corner of the street, I stood admiring her. I thought of all the impromptu conversations I had with her; the old time values I detected that kept her going, kept her walking Benny.

She loathed the insatiable greed of the rich as she loathed greed itself and never spent what she did not have. What she could not pay for, she would wait for until she could. The discipline of thrift had kept her thriving; kept her disciplined to keep walking Benny, to get her out of her house, as clean and tidy as you could imagine; to keep her active and allow the wind and the rain, the cold and the warmth, to make her feel alive, make her meet the world and engage within it.

And as I imagined Benny sniffing his favourite railings for the last time that day, as Mrs Lindley stood in the shadows from the street lights watching him, I feared for what will happen when one of them goes.

Benny will be her last dog, she once said before. But if Benny was to pass these railings for the last time tonight, Mrs Lindley would at least have cared for another living creature and come herself to be that bit nearer, have been prepared that good bit longer, to one day meet again the husband who went before her those sixteen and a half years ago.

A.C. Clarke

is a poet who grew up in London after the War and now lives in Glasgow. Her last full collection of poetry is *A Troubling Woman*. *Droichaid*, a joint pamphlet with Maggie Rabatski and Sheila Templeton, came out last year. All her life she has been aware of the parallel lives going on in cities, the people who fall into the interstices. She was an unmarried mother in the 60s, and had no financial support from her son's father. At that time unmarried mothers did not receive child benefit. She was lucky to be employed in a reasonably paid job but money was always a worry. She has never been able to afford not to work until now, in retirement. She hopes that her own experiences have given her some sympathy with those who are really deprived and particularly those on the margins of society.

The Man with the Plastic Cup

You've seen him everywhere, even when you pretend you haven't. He's young and glassy-eyed; he's prematurely aged by want and weather, he's Scots, he's Roma, he's away with the fairies. He asks you to *'spare change'* with the same monotonous lilt as the old-time rag-and-bone man. Or he looks at you with pleading eyes, says nothing. If you hurry on past him, he may call a blessing after you, a *'have a nice day'* or some such. Or he may shrink deeper into himself like a wounded snail.

Should you drop a coin in his cup, expect a passing stranger to tell you *'they're all on benefits'* or *'he'll only spend it on drugs'* or if the man is Roma, a lurid tale of child sex-trafficking that's doing the rounds on Facebook.

Don't fall for false distinctions between the undeserving and the deserving. For, yes, not every beggar is homeless; and yes, many beggars are brought low by addiction; some even work for gangmasters as they always have. But is there a single human being, however flawed, who deserves this life of endless humiliation, this numbing exposure to the cold heart of the world?

The tabloids will tell you of secret millionaires funding themselves from a gullible public. Good luck to such say I! If they exist they do less harm than all the faceless corporations that lay our planet waste and trap the poor in drudgery and worse, in the name of profit. Drop in your coin, don't tell yourself you are foolish; don't tell yourself you are virtuous. You are flawed and human and a throw of the dice away from destitution.

A Small Packet of Tissues

A pleasant summer evening in Maryhill. Still light at 8 pm. I'd been to a poetry launch in the Mackintosh church and was waiting at a bus shelter for a bus into town. A girl in her late teens was waiting too. Suddenly a group of youths were crowding in, one of them bleeding profusely from his nose. At first I thought he had a nose-bleed. They seemed to know the girl and the one with the bloody nose was clamouring about someone who had attacked him from behind, demanding of the others who it was. His tone was aggressive.

Then they all melted away except for the one with the nose-bleed. He sat shivering on the narrow ledge which bus shelters provide to discourage homeless people from using them as beds. The girl was trying to tend to him.

Plying him with tissues to staunch the flow, which he got through at an alarming rate. I still thought they knew each other. He asked her for money for the bus fare. She refused. He asked me. I too refused, to my shame, imagining it was just a ploy to get money off me. Then the bus came.

He tried to get on, still bleeding heavily, and saying he needed to get to the Infirmary. A woman on the bus gave him the money for his fare. It was clear now that he had a broken nose and was losing a lot of blood. He went up to the upper deck, but when the bus came into Renfrew Street, he came down. He'd exhausted his supply of tissues and was asking people for more. To try to make up for not having lent him the fare, I gave him a pack from my handbag, and said to him that he looked in a bad way and ought to go to the Infirmary.

By now he had decided he wasn't going. He told me he'd been jumped—'attacked' he explained, unnecessarily. He didn't want to go to the Infirmary because his baby had died there. This gave me a shock. I'd have said he wasn't more than seventeen or eighteen—not too young to be a father, of course, but I'd not have put him down as someone with family responsibilities. Also, my baby sister died in hospital and any mention of dead babies strikes a nerve.

He got off the bus near a nightclub and no doubt was going to try to forget it all in drink, though I wondered if he would be let in. I hoped that someone would get him to the A&E department somehow.

I'd seen people bleeding from violent assaults before in Glasgow, and had several strange and unnerving experiences on public transport. He was so young, and for all his bravado so fragile-seeming. I knew the likely bleakness of his future. The brief glimpse of his past was bleak enough. And all I could do was hand him a small packet of tissues, which would be soaked through in no time.

Mary McCabe

was born in Glasgow where she still lives. She taught English before retraining as a careers adviser. This involved interviewing young people in schools and careers offices, and touring workplaces: shipyards, factories and coalmines (*Doon the Careers Office* is based on a true incident).

In 1990 when Glasgow was European City of Culture, Mary accepted secondment to co-write *Streets, Schemes and Stages*, an illustrated account of cultural projects supported by the Social Work Department. She has written the novels *Everwinding Times* and *Two Closes and a Referendum*. Her fictionalised *Stirring the Dust* was Paperback of the Week in the *Herald*. She has also written a children's book and radio plays that have appeared in German translation. She has had many poems and stories published in anthologies and written in Scots, English and Gaelic. Mary is Co-Convener of Pensioners for Independence and a member of International PEN.

Doon the Careers Office

'Monday, 10 o'clock?' Alison raises her eyebrows at Gary. Gary does not react.

'That's fine, Mr MacLeod. Gary'll see you then.' She hangs up. Gary lowers his head. His brow creases.

'So there you go, Gary. Got an interview! By next week you might have a job. Something up..? It's the other direction. You'll not have to cross that scheme where the boys jump you. It's fixed hours, Gary! There's plenty folk out there never know the minute they'll be called in.'

'Gonnae make it anither day?'

Alison groans. 'Monday not suit..? Why d'you not say at the time? I don't want to have to phone him back through the switchboard and everything.'

'Cannae go Monday, but.'

'Why not...? What you doing Monday morning that's more important than going for a job?

'Nuthin.' Face like fizz, gazing at the desk.

'So what is it..? 10 o'clock Monday morning too early for you..? Do you really want a job?

Gary glances up. Is that a tear she wonders?

'Aye,' he says as his head falls down again.

Alison folds her arms. 'Doesn't sound that way.'

'Monday's Da's signin day.'

'Ah, but you don't need your Dad to go with you. You're 16, Gary. Grown up. Trust me, it makes a better impression if you're on your own. Do you know the street? Will I show you on the map?

'Cannae go if Da's doon the broo.'

'Why not?' Gary's face turned crimson...' I'm not a mind—reader. Speak!'

'His shot o the shoes.'

Alison slides her chair back and looks under the desk. Dingy, frayed trainers. Two sizes too big. Alison phones and changes the appointment to Tuesday.

'One more wee thing, Mr MacLeod, if you take Gary on, could you maybe advance him the price of a pair of shoes?'

Imperial by Peter Long

Jim Mainland

Retired teacher Jim Mainland was born in a council house in Lerwick, Shetland. His mother was a 'housewife' and his father a slater and plasterer. He was the first of his family to go to university. Growing up, he heard it said that Shetland was a classless society—it's not—but the strength of community often made it seem that way. His socialism comes from his mother, who taught him that you should always support the underdog, and from his father, whose scepticism and quiet disputatiousness after a pint or two he has inherited.

Imperial

when he gets it into his head

it's like this the meeting off the ferry the taxi the shakedown a fist of fivers stashed upfront a twist of grey taken and trashed and stilled and not under discussion just not or it's hearing the sound of a vow its hushed and holy violence its culled silence and licence to endless and the drag of the daily under the absence and the neighbours know and the neighbours won't so he can dog it out again spreadeagled and pinned and poled or where the reward is a tomorrow where the vein of such and such is an opened flicked obligation bladed with the always more the always more and a debt stacking on nothing squared times the better life of a mimeograph blutacked and battered on the stain of the which bit of the what don't you understand question in the house in the safe house the stabbed in the head house all the better to be pair-hostessed and jobbed and fobbed with first-come first-forced and a new world-view of the catch-up where you play wear this and asking for it and what do you expect or it's the transaction over the phone in the booth on the net on primetime it's class it's careworn chic-tawdry branding the respectable giggle together in a roomful of daily lookings and tasteful stripped paint-me-ups and appliqué with fry-up all-day and shifting nightlies where you become your own currency iron the paper rags see the closing of a door your need's an hour's escape from or a foldback grubbed up inside taking extra profiting the flourish of a you lose game of please and please again and try the dress try it on rewind blanketed repeat your going going gone again under the twisted fact of a lordship church that underwrites the act the fellowship of whose brotherhood's forged heaven stacked stitches up the heart and lips and eyes until what feels like a numbness where the muscle resists takes a beating again and everything's the thing you dread

when he gets it into his head

Geraldine Gould

grew up in Glasgow and graduated in Italian in Edinburgh where she went on to teach in a variety of settings and to bring up her three sons. More recently she completed a Masters degree in Creative Writing at the University of Dundee. Much of her work reflects the prevailing inequalities of racial and sexist discrimination. She is particularly interested in the lives of older women who are so often forcibly retreated from view and whose experiences are also made invisible. Her work is informed by psychoanalytic thinking and the structural influences of society on the individual. She has been a regular contributor to the *Dundee Review of the Arts*. Her poems have been published in *London Grip* and she has two poems in *A Kist of Thistles*. She has read her poems at Live Wire in Dundee and Shore Poets and at the Scottish Poetry Library.

Adagio ma non Troppo

A woman in the choir has a big red and blue tattoo. It reaches a crescendo at her left shoulder, caressing her neck and leaving a trail of leaves and petals as it drops down her back.

She cannot speak, but she can sing. She vaguely knows that no one really knows her or her nickname or her family. No one knows her stories, the tales of all her years. She is not aware that age sits and looks at her. Yet she can feel something pretty close by, waiting, keeping her in, not letting her out.

Singing together, side by side, keeps her in time. There are moments when she is no longer on song, but she keeps moving on, along with the tempo. Here, she can miss the beat, or there, and she remains part of the ensemble.

She turns her head a little to one side so that she can see the three tenors. She smiles warmly at them and catches the eye of one in particular. Something comes back to her with ease. There was always the tempo, the movement. The rhythm keeps her singing now.

Her high gloss nail varnish stays red no matter what. Always has done, since her Craigmillar days.

The big red and blue tattoo is still doing its thing, diminuendo, over her shoulder and down the coda of her back.

Smell the Coffee

She sat in her favourite café, nursing her cappuccino, which was very hot and without chocolate. She liked the way the staff had become familiar with how she preferred her coffee. It somehow made her feel part of something, even a little bit known.

It was a mystery to her why people insisted on putting chocolate sprinkles on their coffee. That made it into a kind of pudding to her, and as a second-generation Italian she did not find that habit at all in keeping with how she had learned to drink coffee. And what was all this drinking cappuccinos in the afternoon about? Never after eleven a.m. her mother had taught her. She imagined these were transatlantic customs, ones she could cheerfully live without, along with a whole number of things about the modern world. Still, perhaps it was all an improvement on the ubiquitous Nescafé of her younger years.

The café was near the university, where decades previously she had been a student herself. She was the first in her family to go to any kind of further education, never mind study for a degree. No one she had been pally with at school had gone on to university either, most of the girls having gone straight to shop or office jobs. In these pre-digital days, it was all about typing skills and redesigning your accent to fit. But she had managed to combine staying within her social group with earning a clutch of Highers, and much encouraged by her Guidance teacher, she had gained a university place.

The university was only a couple of miles from the housing scheme where she grew up, but in some ways it felt like a completely different country. She sat in the café now, watching the student clientele chattering to each other or gazing intently at their laptops. Yes, a different world.

She had taken to coming to the café most mornings, partly to make sure she got out and spoke to people at least once a day, even if it was just to order her coffee.

She enjoyed looking at the young people, and marvelled at their beauty. She wondered if they knew that they were so gorgeous. She remembered never having been satisfied with how she had looked herself at their age, and wondered if in reality she too had been at all beautiful. She remembered her long, thick dark hair, and the shine it used to have, so different from that crinkly texture it had now, although she always made sure it was well cut.

Maybe she had been quite attractive, although she had never felt it. She wasn't now though, that was for sure! What a waste, to not have enjoyed all the gorgeousness of youth at the time. What she would give for it all now, the smooth skin, the hair, the ease of movement, that energy.

She always tried to elongate her stay in the café to make it as long as she could possibly make one cup of coffee last. That was another thing that her Italian background had taught her, treat coffee with respect, enjoy it ma non troppo. She did sometimes think that British people might be a bit mad in the head to drink coffee all day long and into the evening.

On her route home, she saw that the pub on the corner near the main campus square was being renovated. Again. It had been through a few reincarnations over the years. Nothing seems to last very long these days, she thought. The wide entrance doors and the signage above had been removed awaiting more modern replacements, and she had a clear view of the interior as she passed by on the other side of the street. Peeling paintwork underneath the sign over the door was exposed, and she could just make out the first few letters of one of the pub's previous names, MEA. Ah yes, the Meadow Bar.

She crossed over and stopped to peer inside. It was dusty from disintegrating bare plaster and everything was bathed in a strange orange glow from the temporary lighting the workmen were using as they stripped out the fittings from the walls. Their banging and drilling assaulted her ears, but she kept standing there, letting the sound of it slowly and rhythmically fill her body. She was unwilling and then unable to move, as if she were having some kind of dwam or absence...

The drilling noise slowly began to give way to the sound of a crowded pub, full of animated students arguing about the issues of the day; the miner's strike, the three-day week, the hustings for the election of a student Rector. In the far corner, she could just make out a woman with glossy dark hair and a sallow complexion, sitting elegantly on a bar stool. She was being chatted up by a handsome if slightly dishevelled young man.

Wafting around her as she gazed in at the scene she could smell the Nescafé he would offer to her when she agreed to go back to his flat 'for coffee', before a long night of lovemaking, the first of so many ahead for them.

Vikki Carpenter

is a Community Learning and Development worker with Aberdeenshire Council. She has been working from home since March 2020 as well as home-schooling her three children due to her family shielding. She has a daughter who has a congenital heart defect, which makes her high risk. She has also been involved with an 8-week Unison course: Introduction to Creative Writing.

Cannae Complain

Cannae complain about working from home. My office chair, stolen in a mad supermarket sweep raid before lockdown, is only one big wheely push away from the fridge, although as time expands—along with my waistline—the chair's squeaks of resistance are getting louder.

Cannae complain about home-schooling. Children are with us, safe. I can dip into their world of school. Nosy around their study lives rather than clamber the homework iceberg tip. We have laptops and internet, many don't. We are lucky. I know they are working hard. They know they are keeping up with work, which is so important. I tell them how proud I am of them. They don't know I am working even harder to keep up; I don't tell them that.

Cannae complain about my daughter being on the shielding list. Our whole family shielding. It gives me a rule, a reason, legitimate consent to lock up my most precious. And positively dive head first into mummy's protection mode using my invisible cape of love, wrapping them up and keeping them safe. We faced this pandemic head on. Confident of fine-tuned survival skills from living with the life-limiting illness of a child, an unrelenting resilience at our core. We hadn't got this far to get knocked down. We were lucky to stay in.

Cannae complain about the dip in our mental health. It's a big dip. It's been an almighty big dipper of a rollercoaster without the fun. We have plummeted big time, many times. Eight months of five people in a house... and the dog. But we have each other; some people are alone. It has made us verbalise our self-care needs. Express our love. Articulate our feelings. Ask for help. It doesn't always feel it but we are stronger, robust, and more connected from orienteering this pandemic path thrust upon us.

Cannae complain about not going to a shop. I haven't set foot in a shop since the 2nd of March 2020. It feels empowering. No more random wanders around a supermarket looking for inspiration when you're hungry, ending up with bags of things you don't need. Gluttony. We became aware of what we really needed. We overcame our shame and disgust at the amount of money spent on food. We now eat better. We eat what we have and save our money. Fortnightly Asda deliveries are a mammoth feat of project management. PPE to the hilt, everything needing to be wiped and cleaned before entering the house, fridge, cupboards. We are lucky; we have food and are staying safe. Many don't.

Cannae complain about not having a holiday. We have tents so we holidayed in our garden, many, many times. Campfires, marshmallows, songs and games. Three children having fun with their oldies, not a piece of technology in sight and proper toilets! Bonding, growing, and enjoying each other's company. Time to tell stories, pass on family tales and make new memories.

Cannae complain and will not complain, but will endeavour to see the positive that has come from this indescribable tragedy which rocked the absolute foundations of my family life, because we are still standing strong.

Gerda Stevenson

Writer/actor/director/singer-songwriter, works in theatre, TV, opera, radio, and film. Poetry Collections: *If This Were Real* published in Italian as *Se Qeusto Fosse Vero*, by Edizione Ensemble, Rome, 2017, and Quines: Poems in Tribute to Women of Scotland (Luath Press, 1st edition, 2018, 2nd edition, 2020). Her most recent books are: *Inside & Out—the Art of Christian Small* with a biographical introduction and poems by Gerda, and Edinburgh, a collaboration with landscape photographer, Allan Wright. Awards: BAFTA Scotland Best Film Actress for Margaret Tait's *Blue Black Permanent*; winner of the Robert Tannahill Poetry Prize, 2017. Nominations: MG Alba Scots Singer of the Year, for an album of her own songs—*Night Touches Day*; London Festival Fringe Theatre Writing Award, New York League of Professional Theatre Women's Gilder/Coigney International Theatre Award, and three times for C.A.T.S. Awards. In 2018, Gerda gave the Thomas Muir Memorial Lecture (Edinburgh Festival), also the George Mackay Brown Memorial Lecture, Orkney, 2019. www.gerdastevenson.co.uk.

Cat Wumman

A contemporary retelling of an old legend from the swamps
of the Mississippi

I haurdly kent him whan we tied the knot. Ma sister had mairried, ma freend had mairried—the big day ye dreamed aboot. I mean, whit else wis there, yince ye'd rumbled Santa? Mairriage wis the nixt stop on the wey. Ma faimily niver had twa bits o siller tae rub thegither, an it wis the dream, ken—the waddin goon, the limousine wi ribbons, the stacked cake wi the wee bride an groom staunin on tap, unner a booer o fairy flooers.

Ma grandmither wisnae keen. 'Dinnae dae it,' she said when I telt her I wis gettin engaged.

'How no, Gran?'

She jagged me wi her een—yon look that leaves ye wi a skelf—and said, 'Regret's a sair wecht tae cairry aa yer days.'

She wis her ain wumman, ma Gran. Auld fashioned, mind, aye knittin, stitchin an dernin—naethin went tae waste. She had a spinnin wheel, like something oot a story book, makkin her ain wool frae a fermer's wifie wad bring in the spring time. Gran washed it clean in a big pan o hot watter. The hoose wis filled wi thon cosy smell o wet wool. Then, when it wis dry, she'd be at the wheel, clackity—clack, clackity-clack. She learned me how tae dae it. I liked the feel o fleece atween ma fingers and thumb, the slaw release as it spun intae a fine threid, the rhythm o't, ma fit gaun up an doon on the treadle, up an doon, clackity-clack. Sometimes I'd be that intae it, I felt like the wheel wis spinnin ma ain flesh, spinnin me oot o this warld intae anither.

'Look at her,' Mum wad say tae Gran, wi a lauch. 'She's fair awa wi it! She's in a dwaum!'

Mum worked in the hospital—an auxiliary, dishin oot patients wi their bedpans, an aa that. Gran lived wi us, an looked efter me an ma sister at hame. We niver kent oor grandfaither. He left her soon as ma mither wis born. An the same wi Mum. Ma faither didnae hing aboot efter I cam on the scene—twa bairns, baith o us lassies, wis mair nor he could stomach. Sae ye'd think I'd had warnins aplenty no tae gang doon the same road. But life's that twisty ye cannae aye see aheid.

He wis daft aboot me, ma man. I'd niver had a boyfreend that tentie wi me afore. He worked for the cleansin department, an we met on the street. I wis pittin the bin oot for Mum, an I wis late—near missed the lorry. He smiled, cracked a joke, an made me lauch as he picked up the bin. It wisnae lang afore he wis at the door askin me oot. He'd buy me flooers an chocolates, an caaed me his pussy cat.

I like cats. Ma Gran gied me a kitten for ma birthday when I wis wee —big blue een, an lang, smoky grey fur wi daurk stripes. Sometimes, when it wis castin, Gran wad brush aff the bonnie lang fur, an mix it intae the fleece she wis spinnin. I mind I wis disappintit when the wee thing grew up, an didnae want tae play wi the toys I made for her—cotton reels on thried. She'd gie me thon look, like she wis sayin *I'm no yours ony mair. I belang tae masel.* Yin day she went oot an didnae come back.

Onyhoo, that's whit he caaed me—his pussy cat. On the day he gied me the engagement ring, he'd had himself tattooed, wi a cat that looked mair like a panther makkin a wild lowp ower his chest.

'This is you, pussy cat,' he says, unbuttonin his shirt tae show me. 'Yer claws are gruppin ma hert!'

Aa I could think o wis ma bitten nails shamin the engagement ring, an hoo I'd niver had the pooer tae get a grup o onyhin.

Near the same time, a clothin library opened up in the Toon Haa. I heard aboot it frae a wumman wha did the same cleanin job wi me at the school. 'How dy'e mean?' I says. 'Ye cannae wear books, shairly?'

'It's claes—no books, ye daftie!' she lauched. 'They loan them tae ye for naethin. Ye juist hae tae bring them back clean.'

Her son wis mairryin a lassie frae a family that wis loaded. She wis fair in a state aboot lookin dacent, an no shamin her ain family at the kirk. She'd picked oot a swanky goon at this library, matchin shuin an bag, a coat an aa—the hale outfit, fur naethin!

I went doon the Toon Haa tae hae a look. It wis rin bi volunteers, this clothin factory, nice fowk—nae nosey questions. Ye didnae even huv tae show them a voucher like at the food bank, or yer housin benefit letter. They were gey thrang, getting aathing redd up for a fashion show tae raise money. They had tae pey rent tae the cooncil, the wumman in chairge telt me— they didnae get their twa rooms in the Toon Haa for free.

'Weel,' I says, 'I'll come an gie ye a haund if ye like!'

An that wis me—roped in! I fair fancied the notion o a fashion show, mincing doon the catwalk in gear ye can anely dream o! Amazin, the kind o claes on the rails, some o them wi labels I seen on the adverts—big names, an haurdly worn, juist new oot the wrappin.

It wis a nicht no tae forget. Ma Mum an Gran came, an I managed tae persuade ma man an aa. He wisnae keen, but when he heard there wis wine, he cheynged his tune. The drinks an nibbles were aa laid oot on tables, juice for the bairns, wi a box for donations, an a raffle. Some swanky fowk turned up, an they were stuffin notes in the box, no juist coins.

I had tae go doon the catwalk three times in three different ootfits —weel, it wisnae a real catwalk like ye see on the telly, juist a lang cairpet, atween the rows o fowk sittin watchin. The first I wore wis a floaty nightie, wi a silk dressin goon, an sparkly princess slippers. The second wis a ball goon, aa covered in diamonds—I suppose they werenae real, but they looked it. The last wis a faux fur grey winter coat, wi daurk stripes juist like yon wee kitten ma Gran gave me when I wis wee, and lang, black boots. They were that high-heeled, I had tae walk deid slaw tae stey upricht. As I turnt tae gang back doon the catwalk, the coat brushed ma man's knee—he wis sittin in the front row, knockin back a gless o wine—I think he'd had a few—an I lost ma balance. He grabbed me, an stood up, pittin me back on ma feet, an he says tae aabody—'Ma wee pussycat!' like he's showin me aff. They aa lauched. Then he unbuttons his shirt, and pulls it apairt tae show them his tattoo:

'This is her,' he says, wi a big grin, 'stampit on ma hert!'

An aabody claps. Except Gran. She sits there wi a froon on her face that wid gie ye the frichts. I went that reid—ma hale face on fire, as I wobbled awa back intae the cheyngin room.

There wis a lassie there, lookin at herself in the mirror. She wis wearin a bride's goon, wi a veil, an a lang train—pure white satin, wi pearls stitched intae the hale lenth o it, see-through lacy sleeves, an twa linked herts embroidered in lilac on the bodice, juist ablow the neckline—I'd niver seen that afore, something different, an gey classy aboot thae herts. She had a bouquet o silk flooers in her haunds, lilac tae match—a veesion, staunin there, quate, like she's aboot tae say her vows. She wis the same size as me, mair nor less, an I thocht 'Mibbe I'll borrae yon dress for ma ain waddin.' She gied me a smile, an slipped oot the room. I could hear the fowk gie a wee gasp as she floated doon the catwalk.

'Ye fair looked braw in yer gear,' said ma man efter the show. 'Pity ye keeled ower, though!'

I'd noticed the wey he'd gie me a wee pit doon, noo an again. I didnae like it, but I wis uptae ma een getting ma waddin sorted. I wisnae thinkin straight.

Weel, the big day cam. I'd borraed the waddin goon frae the library, an it fitted like a glove. The lilac bouquet cam wi it, an a pair o lilac shuin tae match. I wis aa sortit! He asked whit I'd be wearin—if I looked hauf as guid as the bride in the fashion show, I'd be aaricht, he said. I didnae tell him aboot the borraed goon. Whit a bride's gonnae wear has tae be a secret she keeps frae the groom, ma sister telt me. It's bad luck for him tae ken.

Ma sister cam doon frae the Hielands whaur she's mairried, bidin wi her man, an she did ma hair. Mum gied me a bonnie necklace she'd picked up in a chairity shop roon the corner—it matched the pearls on the goon, an had wee lilac stanes threidit intae it, same shade as the linked herts embroidered on the bodice. I'd managed tae stop bitin ma nails for a hale fortnicht, and ma haunds didnae look sae bad for yince—no quite claws, but no faur aff! I even pit some nail polish on. I wis uptae ninety, though. Gran wis sittin at her spinnin wheel, clackity-clack, clackity-clack, crunchin ma nerves.

'Are ye gonnae get ready?' I says tae her.

'I'm no chillin ma dowp in a kirk ye've niver set fit in juist tae see ye flingin yer future awa!' she says.

Ma sister lifts her een tae the ceiling, an Mum tells Gran tae wheesht.

'Ma wee princess,' she says, strokin her haunds ower the goon's silk faulds. 'Ye'll need tae mind an tak tent no tae spill onythin on it.'

Ma man wis staunin in his kilt, wi the meenister, up at the front. The meenit he seen me walkin doon the aisle I kent something wis wrang. His jaw stertit tae fidge, the wey it aye did when he wis in yin o his moods. An when I made it tae his side, he widnae tak ma haund in his. An I'm thinkin is he gonnae jilt me at the altar? Is he gonnae say 'Naw, I winnae,' insteid o 'I dae?' But he didnae—he said the richt words, deid quate, though, like he didnae want folk tae hear.

He danced wi me anely yince at the hoolie—the first dance—an he wis knockin back the bevvy wi his mates. I could see fowk were whisperin *wis there something wrang?*

That nicht, we gets hame tae his hoose—weel, it's no his, it's the cooncil's—an I'm barely in the door when he rips aff the goon—teirin the seams.

'Whit wis in yer eejit mind, wearin a borraed dress tae shame me? ' he bawls.

I wis dumfounert. It wis juist the opposite! It wis no tae shame him that I borraed it!

'It's the yin yon lassie wore at yer stupit fashion show—a cast aff frae some posh git, an ye daur tae come swannin doon the aisle in it, like the Queen o fuckin Sheeba!'

'But ye said ye liked the wey the lassie looked. I thocht ye liked the fashion show.'

'I wis juist there for the wine,' he says. 'I'll no be a chairity tae mak some fowk wi mair money nor sense feel better aboot theirsels! The fuckin food bank's bad enough!'

I wis sabbin ma guts oot when he cam tae bed. He saftened then.

'I'm sorry, pussy cat,' he says strokin ma back, 'but I see the stuff posh fowk bring tae the dump ivry day. Gear that's worth a fuckin fortune, but tae them it's naethin. I'd no hae their cast affs if ye peyed me.'

I took the goon tae ma Gran tae fix the seams—she could dae miracles wi ripped claes, an she did a rare job. Mum peyed for it tae go tae the dry cleaners, an when I took it back tae the library naebody said a word.

I stopped volunteerin there, though, I couldnae go back, somehoo, efter ma waddin nicht. The shine had rubbed aff aathing. When I wisnae cleanin at the school, I steyed in the hoose—his hoose. It didnae feel like mine.

Gran passed ower, a few weeks efter the waddin—quate, in her sleep. I missed her sair. She left me her spinnin wheel, an I wis gled tae hae it. The clackity-clack wis like her voice had come back tae me. But he didnae like it. Drove him demented, he said. He dragged it, alang wi the wee stool, intae the cupboard unner the stair an pit a lock on the door.

'Dae I get a key?' I says.

'Noo, why wad I be lockin it, if ye had a key?'

'Suit yersel,' I says. 'I suppose ye'll be daein the hooverin, seein it's locked in there in aa?' I stairtit tae answer back.

'Are ye takkin the piss, pussy cat?' he says, an gies me a stoondin dunt on ma breist. 'Ye'll ask fur the key when ye need tae clean.'

Then it's lockdoon. The school closes, an there's nae job fur me. He's still workin wi the bin lorries, so he gets tae go oot tae work, but I'm on ma ain, stuck in the hoose. The anely jaunt for me is tae the food bank. Mum's gien up rentin her hoose, an she's awa tae the Heilans tae bide wi ma sister, whae's expectin her first bairn. I'm aa ma lane. An I'm feart. Buses go by, wi naebody on them but the driver. Maist o the shops are shut. It's like a ghaist toon, yin or twa fowk driftin doon the empty streets, their faces blanked oot wi masks.

He disnae like the food I hae ready for him, when he comes hame at tea time. I cannae please him. Last week he smashed a plate o ravioli at the waa—sauce aawhaur, splattered like bliud. Then he strokes me when we get intae bed at nicht, sayin he's sorry, his hauns rubbin ma breists, ma belly, ma hips, pushin himself intae me, haurd. It's sair. He grunts awa till he's done, then turns ower. An that's him till the morn—sleeps that deep ye'd think he wis deid.

There's a wee black cat comes tae sit on the windae sill. Ma man'll no hae her in the hoose. But the meenut he's awa tae his work, she's wailin at the door—she's got this wey wi her cry, it's near human, an I let her in. I gie her some milk in a wee dish, an then she sits on ma lap an purrs her heid aff while I stroke her. She can tell when ma man's on his wey hame, though, cause she's at the door, askin oot. She's awa doon the road afore he shows up, like she kens tae keep oot his wey.

It's full moon. The wee cat wails frae the street. I ken it's her cry. I lie there listenin. She cannae be wantin in, no wi ma man at hame. It's like she's tellin me something. He's sleepin soond. I get up, an shut the bedroom door ahint me. His tool box is locked up in the cupboard unner the stair. But I mind there's a knife wi a broken tip in the kitchen that'll dae fur a screwdriver, mibbe. An it dis—fits the slits on the screwheids fine. Wi nae soond, I hae the lock aff, an the door appen. An it's there, the spinnin wheel—months sin a seen it—sittin in a pool o moonlicht that's streamin through the haa windae. The wee stool's next tae it, an I sit doon, pit ma fit on the treadle, an aff it gaes, clackity-clack. The threid's still on the bobbin, an a wee bit fleece left tae pit atween ma fingers an thumb, clackity-clack, clackity-clack. It rins oot, though, the fleece, but it disnae matter, for ma skin taks ower. It's peelin aff me in ribbons, windin ontae the bobbin. Black fur, saft an sleek, is takkin its place ower ma banes. Clackity-clack, clackity-clack, till ma skin's aa windit aff me. Ma airms are legs noo, ma haunds an feet saft paws, an ma fingers an taes hae lang, sherp claws. A white-tippit tail whups aboot ma hips.

I hear the bedroom door appen. My man's fitstaps in the haa.

'Pussy cat?' he's caain. 'Pussy cat—whaur are ye?'

An he's staunin there, wi naethin on but his boxer shorts, the moonlicht catchin his panther tattoo. I lowp at his chest, howkin ma claws intae his hert.

'Whit the hell!!' he scraichs, feart oot his wits.

He rins tae the front door wi me clingin tae him, ma claws digging deep. 'Get oot, ye deil!' he skirls, 'get oot!'

An wi yin lang spang, I lowp awa intae the nicht.

Carol McKay

has a new poetry pamphlet 'Reading the Landscape' forthcoming from Hedgehog Press. Her short fiction and poetry have been published widely, from *Gutter* to *Mslexia* and from *Chapman* to *Wasafari*. She was born and raised in the huge post-war housing scheme of Drumchapel in Glasgow. Her parents both worked forty-hour weeks, her dad as a labourer and her mum in a shop. Though it was a loving home, alcohol and 'toxic masculinity' were big factors in her home life, and as a result alcoholism and trauma are recurrent themes in her writing. As the youngest of four, she was able to stay on at school and go to university. She taught creative writing through the Open University from 2004-18 and won the Robert Louis Stevenson Fellowship in 2010. Carol self-published her urban realist, post-pandemic novel *Incunabulum*.

Under Cadzow Bridge

Why is he leaning on the wall, Jack? Doesn't he see it's damp? Look at the moss on it, green and sodden.
BIT OF A REST IS ALL HE'S HAVING.
But his shoulder, Jack. His coat's soaking up the rain. It's running down the wall into his coat.
LEAVE HIM. HE'S TIRED.
It's not good for him, getting his shoulder wet. He's sliding. Look at him, Jack? Why's he sliding?
CAN'T AN OLD MAN HAVE A REST!
Those bricks are snagging his coat. They're rough, Jack. Why doesn't he stand up and walk away?
SHH!
What a day. What a day! That rain. Under the bridge you'd think he'd be safe. Dry. Even though it's November. The sky's so grey: the clouds upending themselves like black bin bags spilling out rain.
IT'S HEAVY WEATHER. THAT'S FOR SURE. HE SHOULD HAVE STAYED AT HOME.
Why didn't he?
WHAT?
Stay at home? With the sky so dark.
CAN'T STAY IN ALL THE TIME. STARING AT TELEVISION.
No.
EVEN AN OLD MAN.
He is old.
TOO OLD TO BE DOWN THERE THEY'LL SAY.
Who'll say?
PEOPLE. AFTER.

White Horses by Mark Penrose

After what?

JUST AFTER.

Look at the bottles, Jack. Even in the burn. And wrappers.

PEOPLE DON'T CARE. DON'T LOOK AFTER THE PLACE.

Is that a bike wheel in the water, Jack? Why's a bike wheel in the water? Look!

IN A MINUTE.

Why do people put a bike wheel in the water? Has a boy lost it? Will he be looking for it?

SHHH!

Will he?

NO ONE'LL BE LOOKING FOR IT. NO ONE COMES HERE, UNDER THE BRIDGE.

But the bottles? How did they get there?

YES, BUT A BOY'S NOT GOING TO BE DOWN HERE. NOT A YOUNG BOY. IN DAY TIME. NOT NOWADAYS.

But the bike wheel?

CHRIST, YOU'RE INSISTENT!

His mouth is open, Jack. Isn't he worried about the rain dripping in? His cheeks are slack. His lips are loose. Purple coloured. He's all purple coloured.

HE'LL BE FINE IN A MINUTE.

Will he pick up his stick? I think it's out of reach. The rain's falling on it. And the big drops from the bridge. Splat! Splat! On the aluminium.

RIGHT AS RAIN IN A MINUTE. JUST CATCHING HIS BREATH.

Why is he down here, Jack?

TOLD YOU. GOT TO GET ON WITH IT. WHAT'S THE GOOD OF STAYING IN?

That must have hurt. He's slipped right down now. Onto the grass and stones. His foot's twisted under him. Is there glass under there? Those broken bottles.

RESTING.

The bottles!

FUCK THE BOTTLES. HE'S HAD HIS FILL OF BOTTLES.

Of course.

AYE. REMEMBER?

He's not like that now.

NO.

But he was then. With the bottles. I remember once—

DON'T TALK ABOUT IT.

Why is he down here? The ground's rough. He could have tripped. Is that what happened, Jack? Did he trip? Did he trip when I wasn't looking? Is

that why he dropped his stick and had to rest?
HE NEEDED A REST. BIT OF PAIN GRABBING AT HIS ARM. SQUEEZING HIS CHEST.
So he came down here? Down the rough path to under the bridge?
IT'S GOOD TO GET OUT.
Here?
LISTEN. LISTEN INSTEAD OF TALKING.
It's all right.
JUST LISTEN!
Sorry.
LISTEN!
I'm listening.
WHAT DO YOU HEAR?
Nothing.
LISTEN.
Water.
I LIVED BY A BURN ONCE. YEARS AGO.
Birds. And far away buses.
THIS BURN. WHAT ELSE?
Pigeons cooing under the arch of the bridge. And a crow—in a tree.
CAN'T SEE IT.
Just hear it.
I DO HEAR IT. WHAT ELSE?
Splat splat drops from the big bridge arch, soaking into the path that's all strewn with bottles and is slimy with leaves.
BROWN LEAVES, EH?
Dead. Dead from the autumn.
YOU DON'T ASK WHY THEY'RE HERE, BESIDE THE PATH; WHY THEY'RE BESIDE THE WATER.
They're leaves. They fell off the trees.
AT THE END OF THEIR SEASON. TALK TO ME.
Talk?
TALK.
So you remember the bottles?
NOT ABOUT THAT.
But you do?
OF COURSE, I REMEMBER. LOTS OF THINGS.
You...
HE.
...did bad things with those bottles.
LEAVE HIM IN PEACE. CAN'T YOU SEE HE'S RESTING?
Now all these bottles are here. Lying at the foot of this wall; at the foot

of this staircase filled up with all the broken bottles, and kebab wrappers, and crushed beer cans and… probably even needles, nowadays. All at the foot of this bridge where no one comes. Broken bottles. Remember?

SHH! LEAVE ME ALONE. SHH! RAIN ON THE WATER.

Jagged green glass. Cheeks running with it. Blood. Dripping. Like the rain, down the faces.

GLASS IN HIS VEINS. GLASS IN HIS HEART. VOICE? RAIN ON THE WATER. DEAD LEAVES.

Jack?

WHAT?

Serve him right, they'll say.

WHO'LL SAY?

People.

AFTER?

After. Broken bottles for a final bed, they'll say.

I'M LISTENING TO THE WATER.

Do you remember, though?

SHH!

It's important.

Not speaking, eh? You. Not he. It's time to acknowledge it.

Jack?

RAIN'S GETTING HEAVIER.

RUNNING INSIDE MY COLLAR.

DAMP THROUGH MY CLOTHES. I NEED TO GET UNDER THE BRIDGE.

VOICE? ARE YOU GONE, VOICE?

OKAY. 'ME'.

That's right, Jack.

ME. HEAVEN HELP ME. WHAT I DID.

But them, too.

THEM?

Him.

I USED TO HIDE FROM HIM.

He was hard, Jack.

WHEN HE ROARED. WHEN HE PUNCHED ME. I USED TO HIDE DOWN HERE AT THE WATER.

Like the man before him.

UNDER THE BRIDGE.

Yes.

LISTENING TO THE WATER.

You listen to the water, Jack. I'll stay till they come for you.

John Wight

grew up in Saughton Mains, a housing scheme in Edinburgh. He left school at 15 and went straight to the dole queue in Thatcher's Britain. Since then he has worked in too many occupations to mention, everything from a warehouseman to a nightclub doorman, to an extra and actor's double in Hollywood. He currently plies his trade as a writer and political commentator.

Please, God

Oh God... it's the sound of his keys in the front door. He's back fae the pub! Please make him be in a good mood the night. Please, God, Oh God, please make it no like last night.

Last night wis bad. Last night I thought he was going tae smash the bedroom door doon wi his bare fists. I wet the bed again, and in the morning, when I tried tae let my Ma know without waking him up, she got angry and woke him wi her shouting and then Dad got angry because he'd been woken and I got hit again.

So please, God, please let Dad be in a good mood for a change. Please let him know it's no ma fault he hates his job and it's no ma fault he's up tae his eyes in debt. And I know he's been caught having another affair, God, but that's no ma fault either.

And why doesn't Ma leave him and make ma life better?

She said she wis gonnae leave him, but she didnae. All they do is argue and fight and then he punches the door and the walls and she throws things and then he turns tae me, telling her it's aw ma fault, that I'm the one tae blame for everything that's wrong wi his life.

But God, all I do is go tae school in the morning and come hame again at night. And when I do come hame, and Dad's in the living room, I can feel his disappointment when I walk in. He makes a noise whenever he sees me sitting in an armchair, asks me if I'm gonnae be there aw fucking night, and then he always finds some excuse tae hit me again.

God, it's only when Dad goes off tae work on the rigs for two weeks that things are fine. Then I don't pee the bed, then I can go tae sleep without having tae worry about his key in the front door and me listening tae see what kind of mood he's in after drinking in the pub aw night. And it's when he comes hame fae the pub and he's been drinking whisky that things get really bad.

God, why don't you stop him drinking whisky? Aye, that's it; that's it, God! Just stop my Dad drinking whisky and everything'll be okay and fine.

Ma's crying aw the time and when she isnae crying she's shouting at me. It's no me, God. Please tell her no tae take it out on me. Please. I can't go anywhere else. I need tae stay here; this is ma home and I live here. So please, God, please tell my Ma no tae take it out on me.

Dad's always screaming that I'm a little bastard, that if it wisnae for me holding him back he could do this and that. He says I'm just a spoiled wee bastard, that I'm a mummy's boy and that when he wis my age he wis better than me. Much better.

I just can't understand it. All this seemed tae start when Dad first got the job on the rigs and started being away for two weeks at a time. After a few months he began staying away for three weeks, phoning hame and telling my Ma he wis doing an extra week's overtime instead of coming hame like he wis supposed tae.

That's when things started tae go wrong. What wis supposed tae be a happy time, wi money coming in and my Ma talking about moving out of the scheme tae a better place, became a bad time. She started drinking and when she drinks she gets bad tempered and when she gets bad tempered, God, she takes it out on me.

When I grow up I promise I'm going tae make sure I don't do this tae my kids. It's just no fair! Last week, when I walked intae the living room on ma way tae the kitchen for a snack, Ma turned on me wi the leather belt she keeps on the back of the door and started whipping me across the back and shooders wi it.

Sometimes I want tae run away, God. Honest, sometimes I want tae just get as far away from here as I can. But if I do and they catch me I'll be sorry for the rest of ma life. That's what Ma always tells me, God, that if I misbehave I'll be sorry for the rest of ma life.

All I want is for us tae be a happy family just like the families on the telly. They never scream at each other; the bairns in those families never get whipped wi a leather belt or shouted at. And when they do argue they always end up laughing about it after. Why can we no be like that? Why?

It'll be Christmas soon. I hate Christmas. I know it's your son's birthday, God, but I'm sorry, I really hate it. Last year Ma woke me out of bed early on Christmas morning. She'd just had a phone call from a wumman in Dundee telling her that my Dad was lying in her bed and that he wis staying wi her fae now on and wisnae coming hame again.

Ma wis greeting on the couch, rocking back and forwards wi her head in her hands. I wis scared and peed masel again. And then Ma went berserk and took a hammer tae the furniture and began smashing and destroying everything. And I wis even mair frightened, God, frightened of what she'd do if somebody didnae stop her and maybe I should've, God, but I wis too scared.

And then later in the day Dad arrived hame and Ma told him tae pack his bags and get out. And he wis very quiet and he looked at me sitting on the couch and asked me tae move some of his things doon tae the car. And when he did ma legs were shaking and I looked at Ma and she looked at me and I looked at Dad and said no.

That's when he went mad again. He walked over and slapped me hard on the face, screaming that I wis an ungrateful little bastard speaking tae him like that and that he had a good mind tae spread me all over the fucking wall. My Ma was sitting on the armchair crying, drunk from all the cans of lager she'd been drinking aw day, and I really thought about jumping through the windae, God. Just tae show them I couldnae take any mair, show them how what they were doing wisnae fair and that they had no right, no right...!

I wish I wisnae so afraid. I really hate myself sometimes for being this scared.

At school the other boys seem happier than me. I look at them and wonder about their mums and dads, wonder if any of them lie in bed at night scared like me. Sometimes I think I want tae tell someone. But I cannae. The teachers arenae interested in me anyway; they're only interested in the clever ones and I'm no one of the clever ones.

God, I dinnae have any friends and I dinnae want any. I just want everyone tae leave me alone; everyone except you. I want you tae be ma friend and I wish I could see you and touch you.

But I know I cannae and it doesnae really matter, God, because I know you're up there and can hear me. I like talking tae you, God, and I like the fact you willnae tell my Ma and my Dad what I'm saying.

God, promise me one thing. Promise me you'll speak tae them and tell them tae stop arguing and fighting aw the time. Promise me, God, please promise. If you do I promise I'll be good from now on. I will, I'll go tae church and I'll do anything you want. Honest, God, I will, I really will; honest I will, God. Only please speak tae them tae make them stop. Please, please, please make them stop.

God, why do I want tae kill myself sometimes? Maybe it's because I want tae be in heaven beside you. But if I kill myself I know you'll be very angry and I dinnae want you to be angry wi me, God. I want you tae like me and let me sit beside you, like in the pictures at school, you wi your big white beard and all the angels in heaven. You wouldnae shout at me, would you, God? You dinnae drink whisky or lager... you dinnae come hame fae the pub in a bad mood and start shouting and screaming, do you?

I've got a big sister, God, but she's married and lives somewhere else now. Her name's Fiona and if Fiona wis still here it widnae be so bad because Dad loves Fiona. I know he does because he never shouted at her when she lived here. She could do anything and it wis always okay wi him.

One final thing, God, please dinnae let me turn out like him.

Brian Hamill

was a writer and editor, living in Whiteinch in Glasgow. He grew up in Airdrie, and spent years working in factories, call centres, shops and restaurants, before eventually graduating as a mature student from the University of Glasgow with a degree in Information Technology. Brian won the Scottish Book Trust New Writer's Award for Writing in the Scots Language in 2013, and his collaboration with the novelist Alan Warner, a collection of prose entitled *Good Listeners*, was released in 2019. He has had stories published at various times in places such as the *Edinburgh Review*, *Tangerine Press*, and *New Writing Scotland*. Much of his time was spent running his small independent press, The Common Breath, which has produced publications by renowned artists such as Tom Leonard and A.L. Kennedy.

Sadly, earlier this year, as the anthology was being put together, Brian died.

Donald's Da

Your best mate is a wee guy from the quadrant called Donald. His full name is Donald Dunn. So is his da's, but he gets called Big Don. You, and the rest of your pals, really prefer the da. Donald is wee and fat. His nose runs all the time, he's in the bottom group for language and sums, and the lassies hate him. But everybody in the scheme loves the da. Big Don doesny wear shirts or jumpers, only football strips. He has loads of them, some real, some fake. His hair is short at the top and long round the back and sides. He has a King Billy tattoo, like the older lads at your school are getting now. Big Don used to work, but now he doesny because he has agoraphobia. His maw has a bad back and depression, so she's home all the time as well. Big Don can go to the offy for the lottery or the paper, but anywhere else and the agoraphobia kicks in, so he never goes further.

Big Don is wee and skinny, but he talks like one of you. He says our scheme thinks it's hard, but it's the fucking Blackpool Pleasure Beach compared to where he came fae. He grew up in the city, where even the maws were hard as nails, where the polis got chased out the streets regular, where gangsters controlled everything and you never, ever spoke in public unless it was around people ye knew. Big Don only moved out here to be with Donald's maw once she was pregnant, but also because he needed to get out of the game, it was eating him up. He was becoming a marked man. A known face. Polis following him, taking photos, the heat was on him alright. Big Don says the top boy in our area, Jon Jo Knox, wouldny dare mess wi him, even though he'd no back-up out there. It's all in the way ye carry yourself, he said. You asked your da what that meant and he said it was all tall tales. You asked your maw what that meant and she said never mind, Donald's family were good folk.

Big Don invited you all in to watch the wrestling with Donald when it was on, coz he knew nobody else had satellite. When you got a wrestling boxset out the video shop and watched it at home, your da laughed and asked if you wereny too old for that. Your face stayed red and hot for hours.

Nobody ever felt like watching it with Donald's da. He knew all the special moves, and he could tell as soon as somebody's walk-in music started who it was coming to the ring. He agreed with Donald that the standard was starting to slip and that the Hulk would've tanned all these new, younger ones.

*

When Rangers win the league, Big Don drinks a three-litre bottle of Strongbow then climbs halfway up a lamp-post and shouts 'Get it up yeez, ya filthy fuckin bastards!' You're laughing, bangin the front window, hoping to catch his attention, but he's waving over at somebody else and your maw pulls you away in case Big Don sees and comes over.

Donald's ma is a Catholic but Big Don tells you not to hold it against her, it's no her fault, and he laughs and you laugh tae.

You know about Donald going up the high flats to see Lisa Scanlon before his da, or anybody else. Donald makes you promise you won't tell. You go to Rose Hall and Lisa Scanlon goes to St Luke's, and you've been seeing her on the way to school for years. Lisa is two years older than you's, and she isn't ugly. She's tall and thin and dark, and she always smiles when you pass her, and you're shocked, really shocked that she's letting Donald Dunn, wee snottery Donald, go up to her place when her maw and da are out and get aff wi her in her bedroom. Donald tries to tell you what a lassie's tit feels like but you don't want to hear it, not from him. You say that if you get curious, you could just stick your hand up his T-shirt. Your diddies are well bigger than Lisa's, you say, just to make sure he gets it. Donald smiles, because he knows you're jealous.

When you see people running up the street to Donald's, you belt out the front gate and go too. Big Don is out in the garden swingin a cricket bat round his head. You wonder where he got the cricket bat from. Nobody has played cricket here, ever. Donald is sitting on the front steps, greeting.

Donald's maw is telling Big Don to calm down, and his big sister Lesley is saying she'll pull Lisa's hair out by the roots. Aw the weans from the scheme are in the garden or just outside on the pavement, everybody's there, excited as fuck. Wee Alan Paton tells you that Lisa's granda, Charlie Scanlon, came home early and caught her and Donald. He punched Donald in the mouth and called him a wee orange bastard and threw him down the stairs. Big Don swings the bat hard so it swooshes through the air, and he shouts out that he'll do time for the bastard that touched his laddie.

You hear whispers and see folk turning to the left, and it's Jon Jo

Knox coming down the hill. The talking stops. Jon Jo looks massive coming in the front gate and going up to Big Don. You crowd round to listen, when Jon Jo tells Big Don he's heard all about it and he'll go up the flats wi him in case any Fenian fucks try tae jump in. Big Don doesny say anything. Donald's ma says his da cannae go because he's agoraphobic and because his temper'll get the better ay him. Jon Jo shrugs and tells her he's away up to sort that auld bastard out anyway. He vaults over the fence and starts jogging in the direction of the highrisers. You're torn between wanting to see Charlie Scanlon dragged out his flat and flykicked all over the road, and finding out what Big Don is going to do. Donald's da still doesny talk. He looks at the ground. Then he puts the bat down and goes in and shuts the door. You ask Donald how his da's agoraphobia doesny stop him from being outside. Donald tells you to shut it, but wee Al laughs and says Big Don shat it. Shat it to go up tae Charlie Scanlon, who was blinded by the big bang. Who got bullied at school by Cain and Abel. People start laughin and Donald is crying again and goes in.

You run home to tell your da the story. But he gets angry and says that Big Don doesn't have to let you into his house to watch the satellite, he does it because he's a good guy. Your da says fighting isny what makes a man. The next day you write BIG DON = MULLET SHITEBAG on a bit of paper and put it through their letterbox. Donald never brings it up, but you know he knows your writing.

Peter Bennett

is a working-class writer and musician from Tollcross, in the East End of Glasgow. He left school at fifteen and worked in a variety of jobs before returning to education at twenty-one. He studied at Paisley University until the third year of a BA in Sociology. Owing to personal problems at the time, he never completed the degree. He found work as a scaffolder through a friend's company and worked in that field until retraining as a Health and Safety Advisor. He lives with his wife and children in East Kilbride, just outside Glasgow.

A Hauf an a Hauf

The cauld air slaps ma cleanly-shaven face as ah step oot intae the front gairden. No in a bad way, ye unnerstaun. It's good tae feel such a vibrant sensation in the morning—well it's good tae feel it anytime, ah suppose. Still here Arthur, still livin the dream. Aye right. Still, it's good tae huv a sense ay humour.

Ah'm gaun tae collect ma pension fae the Post Office, ye see. Then ah'm meetin ma auld pal Tam O'Henry—wan ay the only wans left, as a matter ay fact.

The gairden is covered in a thick frost, which gies it that crisp, fresh, sparkling quality. It has tae be said, it looks better noo than it does in full summer bloom. At least the overgrown, frost covered grass conceals the rapidly accumulatin collection ay rubbish the local bloody haufwits like tae fling oer the hedge whenever the notion takes them. Bloody animals. Nae respect, the bloody swines. They widnae've dared years ago cos they'd huv goat a bloody good hidin fur that kinda kerry oan, ah'll tell ye.

It's the gairden ye see, it's no as well looked efter these days. No since ma Jeanie died.

For the first few years it wis awright. Ah'd be oot weedin and cuttin grass. Trimmin the bushes in the spring and prunin the roses under the windae. Ah actually enjoyed it, kept me busy. Truth be told, ah wished ah'd done mare ay it wae Jeanie—ye know, helped her oot in the gairden—when she wis here. That wis always her thing though. Jeanie loved aw things horticultural. We were overjoyed when the Cooncil offered us this hoose. A lower cottage flat they wid cry it noo. Four in a block we cried it. Wan building, split intae four dwellings. The upper wans each have their ain gairden tae the rear, wae the lower wans havin wan at the front.

That wis it for us. We had the hoose wae oor ain gairden and we were happy here. Ah suppose thinking aboot it noo, the very process ay keeping the gairden as close tae her exactin standards as ah could, made me feel somehow closer tae her.

Whit wis the point ay this again? Aw aye, ah'm no as young as ah used tae be. Ah'm no as able for the gairdenin, ye see. Ah try and see whit ah kin of course but ah'm seventy wan years of age. Ah'll huv tae get oan tae the Cooncil an tell them ah need help.

Naw ah won't, in fact. There's no chance ah'm phoning that shower ay bloody arseholes. They just want me oot ma ain hoose so's they kin gie it away tae some bloody work-shy brood ay reprobates. Happenin aw oer, so it is. Ah've seen it!

When Jeanie died it didnae take them long afore it wis 'Mr Coyle, you may want to consider the new Sheltered Housing complex on Edrom Street. It's really a marvellous development. If you would just have a look at the brochure here I'm sure you will find it to be most accommodating'. Fat bloody chance! 'Ah'm gaun naewhere!' ah told them. Ma Jeanie and I stayed here fur oer forty year. Waited another ten afore that oan the waitin list. 'It's no just somewhere tae staiy', ah told them. 'It's mare than that.

This hoose hauds a lot of memories fur me. Memories ay the times ma Jeanie and I had here. Yer no gettin me intae wan ay they homes. The only waiy ah'm leavin here is in a boax'. That wis five years ago noo. Christ, is it really that long awready? Aye. It must be. The winter ay nineteen ninety-two it wis, when she passed, twelfth ay January. It's March noo, ninety-seven.

Everythin in the hoose is as it wis when Jeanie passed. Ah like it that waiy. Another waiy that ah kin feel close tae her, ah imagine. Ah'll no be here much longer anywaiy. Whit's the point in rearranging things noo? Mind you, ah mind sayin that tae masel five years ago an aw.

An easier objective tae achieve ye might say. Change nothin inside. Keep it as it wis, thereby conserving her memory. Ah never liked hauf the ornaments an souvenirs she'd amassed oer the years if ah'm completely truthful. That wis the point though; they were her ornaments, her collection ay tea towels brought back fae anywhere we—or anyone deemed close enough tae us tae warrant asking—ever went. Ah wis the breadwinner, Jeanie wis the homemaker. That's how it wis in oor day. By that definition then, they had tae staiy.

By a gairden's very definition or at least that ay a livin plant, it had tae change, had tae grow, expand, encroach even. Only by human manipulation is it tamed, shackled back, neatly pruned and delicately cared fur. Cared fur like Jeanie cared fur this gairden. No this example ay overgrown suburban jungle that remains. Still though, it disnae look hauf as bad wae its mornin frost coverin.

The space in the hedgerow where the gate lies is ever diminishin, the hedge reaching oot through the air oan each side an graspin oot at its opposite number in an attempt tae become wan.

Frost faws aff ay the leaves an layers a dustin oan ma shooders an sleeves as they catch and scrape against the fibre ay ma overcoat.

Ah begin tae tentatively head up the hill taewards the Co-operative oan Shettleston Road, tryin no tae go oan ma bloody erse. Chic McHendry fell oan this slope last year an broke his bloody hip. The aulder ye get, yer bones turn tae dust, ah'm tellin ye—aboot as rigid an robust as a bloody Weetabix.

We approach the Portland Arms, Tam an I. It's just past hauf past wan. The façade ay the building husnae changed a bit since it wis built in nineteen thirty-eight. Fae the pavement up tae the bottom ay the windae sills and surrounding the door, the waw is comprised ay black an grey granite. Above the doorway is the sign Portland Arms in stainless steel letterin, backlit by red neon light. The remainder ay the waw at the front ay the buildin is constructed wi red facin brick wae stane copin.

Enterin the main door, we immediately arrive in a small vestibule where there ur two doors—wan tae the left and wan tae the right. These two doors were originally, ah would surmise, put in place fur ease ay access tae either end ay the circular bar held within.

Part ay Tindal's vision, ye see? Naw well, ah don't suppose ye dae. Jonathan Tindal wis the proprietor back when he built his incarnation ay the pub in nineteen thirty eight. It wis tae replace the auld pub ay the same name that stood next door. Bit ay a visionary ye see, auld Tindal. He decided that a pub should be expansive wae lots ay room for patrons tae be seated rather than be crowded roon a bar as wis the case in many ay the surrounding pubs ay the time. Accordingly, he promptly acquired the tenement block next door tae the auld pub, demolished it and built wan mare attuned tae his philosophy.

Where wis ah then? Oh aye, the two doors. As ah said, there ur two doors as ye arrive, wan at either side. We take the wan tae the right. This takes us intae the Celtic end. The other door as ye may or may no have gathered, takes ye intae the Rangers end.

Hardly in keepin wae Tindal's vision for the modern publican then. He obviously never accounted for the entrenched sectarian divisions ay this city at the time ay inception.

Ah personally, care not a jot fur such segregation. Ma ain faither wis spat oan in the street as he searched fur work when he came oer fae County Donegal in nineteen twenty-three. Ah've witnessed countless acts ay violence borne fae the ignorance ay bloody eejits oan baith sides ay the fence. They kin bloody keep it! It is however, a segregation ay choice ah should point oot. Ah mean, there's nae doormen staunin there directin folk tae their delegated section an there's nae real risk involved in crossing tae the other side, as it were. Rather, it's an arrangement that has evolved naturally an organically. It should be applauded in a city wae countless pubs affiliated tae either ay the Auld Firm. Everyone is seemingly happy wae the continued modus vivendi an there's nae mare trouble in the Portland than in any other pub. Still though, we're creatures ay habit, Tam and I, and wae names like Coyle and O'Henry there wis only wan door we were gaun tae use.

Through the door, the customary aroma ay tobacco smoke an insipid, stale beer greets us like an auld friend. A strangely comforting sensation that comes wae familiarity. Horizontal layers ay grey smoke hing in the air like ghostly apparitions, hoverin seemingly indefinitely as each layer is renewed cyclically by the relentless puffin ay the patrons throughout the bar. Tam goes tae the bar tae order oor drinks. A hauf pint ay heavy an a hauf ay Glenfiddich wae watter fur me. Tam's usual is a hauf pint ay Tennent's lager an a measure ay varyin whiskies dependin oan baith his mood, an his finances.

Lookin aroon the surroundin tables, ah kin observe aw ay the usual faces. At this time ay the day, it's largely pensioners an unemployed in fur a couple ay drinks tae while away the hours an drudgery ay their day. The sad thing is, occasionally wan ay the faces disappear. People die, life goes oan. Some ay the mare popular characters may even get a commemorative plaque, mounted in memoriam, at their favoured seat or stool at the bar. Ah acknowledge the friendly faces ah see; ah nod ay the heid or a cursory wink. Maist offer some sort ay recognition; a raised glass or smile in response. Some however, just stare blankly, unwillin tae enter intae any type ay social interaction. Ah've largely gied up tryin tae talk tae the young yins that come in. Maist feign the slightest ay interest in any subject matter ye try tae ignite conversation wae afore buggerin aff as soon as possible. They're no aw as polite as that though. Some ay the youngsters prefer tae blatantly ignore the opinions held by masel an other elderly people, preferring instead tae shun ye entirely. The erosion ay common courtesy an respect fur yer elders in this country ah put it doon tae. It just didnae happen in ma day but there ye go, times change. Mibbe it's me though; ah mean who'd want tae listen tae an auld bugger like me rabbitin oan. It's just hard tae accept ah suppose. Ah mean, it wisnae always like this, ye just get aulder an it seems ye become less relevant tae people.

There's wan shinin light, ma young grandson. Twinty years auld he is, a strappin big lad. Ma only grandchild an the only real family ah've goat left. His faither—ma son, died ye see. He goat in wae the wrang crowd an started messin aboot wae the drugs. Died because ay that bloody shite when the boay wis just eleven year auld. Daniel wulnae go doon that road though, ah'm certain ay it. He's a bright lad, that yin an nae mistake; sais he might drap in an see me the day, in fact.

Wan ay the aforementioned ignorant wee bastarts is oan ma seat when ah get tae it. Tam an I ayeways sit here when we're in. 'Dae ye mind shiftin son, yer oan ma seat', ah sais tae him. 'Aye? Ah don't see yer name oan it', he sais. 'Ye might huv soon enough when ye croak it though ya nauld bastart', he sais, laughin wae his pal an pointin tae the plaque at the next table.

'You'll huv an embossed imprint ay ma boot oan the cheek ay yer erse if ye don't sling yer hook ya cheeky wee bastart!' ah sais tae him, nae respect these swines. He stauns up lookin as if he's goat something else tae say fur himself afore pickin up his pint an noddin tae his mate afore the two ay them bugger aff, movin alang a few tables. Bloody swines.

Ah'm bloody hoachin fur a drink noo efter that kerry oan. Where's Tam went tae fur them, the Wellpark Brewery?

He's staunin at the bar talkin tae some bloody big brute ay a fella, bletherin away. Ah'm ready fur gien him a shout but he starts makin his waiy taewards me kerryin the drinks oan wan ay they wee circular trays ye get in pubs, stoappin tae blether tae mare people sittin at the tables he passes oan the waiy. 'Will you stoap natterin tae every bugger in the bloody place an get oer here wae they drinks', ah sais tae him oer the hum ay the many voices in the room.

Efter whit seems an inordinate amount ay time he eventually gets here, puttin the tray oan the table an sittin doon. 'Whit bloody took ye?' ah sais. 'Ah'm bloody parched'.

'Stoap yer moanin Coyle! Ah'm entitled tae say hello tae a few people. That's whit the pub's fur—socialism', he sais. Ah take ma drinks an decide against pursuin it any further. He's right, ah suppose. Cannae really argue wae that. 'Who wis the big fella ye were talkin tae at the bar?' ah sais.

'Aw aye, him. Nice big fella, never caught his name', he sais.

Des Dillon

is an award-winning poet and has performed across Europe, Russia and America. His writing is critically acclaimed, popular and sometimes controversial, often addressing the elitism that creates underclasses. He wrote *Singing I'm No a Billy He's a Tim*, considered Scottish Theatre's most successful contemporary play. He won The Lion and Unicorn prize for the best of Irish and British literature in the Russian language. Working class and a product of the Coatbridge Irish, he is a natural storyteller, as is evident in his classic novel *Me and Ma Gal*, which is listed on the Hundred Greatest Ever Scottish Books.

Ten-Pound Note

He kept saying he didn't understand me but I bit my tongue, spelled out my name, address and date of birth and set the visit for three days later.

I always feel I've lost something when I cross the border, like I'm moving completely into another space. It was a long drive and when I pulled into Westmoreland for a coffee, a guy in a wheelchair was in the doorway shaking a tin. I made a hand gesture that meant *I've no change but will give you what coins I have on the way out*. It's funny how much you can say with your hands.

They were doing thermal mugs for one ninety-nine and I thought one would cheer me up a wee bit. As I paid, I remembered the guy in the wheelchair and hoped she'd give me enough change not to be embarrassed. It was a ten-pound note and a pound coin.

—Merry Christmas, the guy said when I dropped the coin in.

—Aye, same to you, mate.

When I walked away, I had that tension you get in your chest before you cry. I got into the safety and solitude of the car and watched him. He looked cold in his wheelchair as I transferred the coffee into my new thermal mug. It fitted in the hole in the dash perfect, but even though it was a great thing, it didn't take the edge off my feelings. The temperature was hovering at zero and you could already see darkness coming in, red and black, from the east. The coffee was cool enough to drink by the Kendal cut-off. It was good to be warm and cocooned in that car with sleet on the windows like sand and the wind trying to shunt me over. I passed an artic lying on its side, the crash barrier twisted like tinsel.

I was going to bite my tongue if it was the phone guy, but it was three women and they were helpful. I asked if I could hand in an AA book.

—Is it biblical?

—Biblical?

—Only books can be handed in are biblical.

—I suppose it can be considered as biblical, in a way.

The three of them gathered and flicked through. One got on the phone and as she enquired, another checked my ID and told me about the procedure. I was in luck, the one on the phone said. They were in a good mood and I could hand the book in. Then, as an afterthought, she asked if I had a pound coin.

—Pound coin?

—For the locker.

I had a ten-pound note and a credit card. They explained you put your car keys, money and valuables in a wee locker.

—They won't let you in without a pound coin, did no one tell you that? she said. You get the pound coin back when you leave.

—I know I'm Scottish but I'm not worried about the pound coin. I'm hardly going to worry about a pound coin, am I?

There was a silence where they didn't know whether to laugh. I don't know how long that lasted but it got me thinking how time speeds up as you get older but this last month, since he got put in, time has slowed right down for me. Every day I'm counting.

A bus drew up.

—There's the bus. Ask the bus driver for change.

He was counting money when I tapped the door and he reached out and hissed it open without changing position. It was his eyes that swivelled. There was one old woman and a young guy on this bus.

—Don't have change of a ten-pound note, do ye?

He clicked pound coins from one hand to another with a magician's dexterity but the rhythm stopped at seven and he said, 'is it a Scottish note?'

It was.

—Can't take Scottish notes.

I went to speak but nothing came out.

—Not legal tender, he said, and pushed his bottom lip up against his top.

I was going to say, listen mate, my son's in there, I've travelled two hundred miles to see him, I'm tired and I'm emotional and I need a pound coin to get in but he thrashed the coins into some metallic thing and although the rage came up and exploded in my shoulders, I stayed calm.

—Cheers, mate, I said, and got off. The doors hissed then thumped shut.

—He doesn't take Scottish notes, I said to the women. One of them whipped out an English tenner but the bus drilled off. You could see they were disgusted. One of them used to live in Scotland, she said, Kirkintilloch, she said, no wonder they hate us, she said, the Scots, with people like that, she said. And that's when they chipped in, these three women, from their own purses and turned my Scottish tenner into five pound coins and a load of smash for the drink machines in the hall. I left with two things; pride in keeping my temper and warmth for these women.

I should've expected the search. Arms up and some guy putting me down. Trouser legs. They diminish our rights, our sons and daughters, when they get the jail. Sure enough I used the pound coin to lock my stuff in a wee glass locker, then they sent me to a guy with a black Labrador standing in the middle of a yard.

—Move forward and stand on one of the yellow squares please, sir.

I did. He brought the dog up and of course it sniffed my balls right away. Most dogs do that. My instinct was to clap its velvet head but the handler must've sensed it cos he said, 'Keep your hands by your sides please, sir.'

He was Scottish and I wondered if the guy who answered their phones could understand him.

—Been here before, sir?

—No.

—Make your way up those stairs. You'll come to a room with some seats. Wait till someone comes and gets you.

—Cheers mate, I said, but there was no reply. He stood with the dog in such a way I thought he'd been a long time in the military.

At the top of the stairs a screw was waiting and he led me in. It was bright mainly because all the cons had bright red boiler suits. I spotted Dan five tables away with a big smile.

—Da, he shouted, and the tension in my chest came back but I battered it down and walked easy, like it was McDonalds on a Saturday afternoon and I sat down. He looked better than I'd seen him for years.

—How's things?

—Alright.

—What's it like in here?

—It's good.

—Good?

—It was boring at first but I'm a cleaner now.

—Fucksakes Dan — you've got a job?

—Aye, it was twenty-three hour a day bang-up but not now.

When he said that, I remembered guy after guy, through the years, saying it. Twenty-three hour bang up. I'd even said it myself, it was a language, a badge, a sign for a whole other culture. Twenty-three hour bang up. Sometimes it was lock-up. These are the things I thought as Dan told me about his job.

—I'm up at seven, he said. Out dishing out the grub, eat as much as I like, then cleaning all day, back at night to my cell.

—What's that like?

—My cell? Bed, telly, X-Box.

—X-Box? I can't even afford an X-Box.

—It's a canter, Da.

That was the last thing I wanted to hear. I wanted him to be having a hard time and never want to step in jail again but he read my face.

—I don't mean I actually *like* it, Da. It was shite at first, but since the Manchester boys got me a job it's been easier. Means I don't think about getting out all the time. I just go from day to day.

I don't know if that was true or just for my sake. He told me he'd been befriended by these lifers who had recommended him for a job. Lifers. I could see his thin ice cos I'd been out on it myself for a long time. He was saying he was going to stop drinking, get a job, sort his life out. He was saying all the right things with the wrong heart.

There was nothing I could say so I made that visit as entertaining as I could. Told him crazy stories about my brother's wife dying with the drink, what the funeral was like, all the old battered faces turning up from my past. Got him laughing. Head tilted back, wide-open mouth, laughing. There were times where I forgot where we were. We could've been in McDonalds except his hands were trying to wash themselves as we spoke. It's funny how much you can say with your hands. I asked if his mother had been in.

—Three times.

—How does she take it?

He shrugged.

—Does she cry?

—No. Ye fuckin joking? I told her on the phone. See if your maw cries, ye get a right slagging for it. They've got to be told, the maws, not to cry.

—What if your Da cries? I said, and we burst the tension of that room again with our laughter.

—That's the worst thing that can happen, he said, still laughing.

When it was time I asked if it was okay to hug him.

—It is Da, he said, but if ye do they'll give me a strip search when I go back through.

And he nodded to some vague place beyond the bars. I said goodbye but didn't say *love you*, cos I didn't know if that would get him a hard time. It was difficult looking cool as I left and I wondered if I was feeling worse than him.

Back in the car the dregs of the coffee were warm and I drank it looking at the jail through sleet and drizzle. When I drove out of the car park the same bus driver was indicating to pull out onto the road. I flashed him out and, as he swung round, he looked at me with a half-finished wave and a look of recognition on his face.

Andy Crichton

is originally from Glasgow and now lives in Fife. He is a retired community worker, having worked with 3 local authorities, a housing advice charity and the WEA. Following retirement he returned to college to study Art & Design. He has been an active trade unionist and campaigner throughout his working life and is currently a member of Unite, presently serving as the acting chair of Unite Community in Fife. He is also a member of the Labour Party and actively involved in Fife People's Assembly, an anti-austerity campaign group.

Dominie

'Right—don't start me!' Naw, it's him again—my da! Me and my pals were aw meant to be meeting up at Marie's cos she got the new David Essex LP for her birthday but, naw, in he comes, givin it, 'Right you, upstairs and get yer homework done...' Honestly, it's no fair, it just isnae.

Y'know what he's like, sauntering in after work sayin he's tired— but no too tired right enough to stop aff at the social club on the way hame. Few drinks wi his mates, talkin mince about fitba and rattling on about Ted Heath bein the best Prime Minister we've ever had. Then comes back in and before you know it he's asleep in front o the telly. Honestly, I just don't get him at times, I really don't.

The homework? It's for Mrs Mackin—she's our Modern Studies teacher. Naw, she's no too bad as it happens. Anyway, she's been doing stuff on what happened at the shipyards on the Clyde two years ago—remember the government wanted to shut the yards down but the workers there just took them over and kept on working? It saved loads o jobs aw the way along the river. It wis great, like the workers organised everything themselves — 'There'll be nae bevvyin!'—loved that! Anyway, Mrs Mackin was talking about the differences that made tae aw these communities and so she wants us tae write something about people in our family, or other folk we know, who've done something that's made a difference. God, I know, murder, eh? I wouldnae know where tae start wi something like that.

Mind you, I mind my ma sayin that my granda worked in the yards when he wis younger. Aye, I still really miss him though, but that's been a few years now. Anyway, he wis a hammerman—a pretty dangerous job my ma says. Naw, he had tae stop workin cos o him gettin shot in the airm.

Naw, he did really, I'm tellin you—he got shot but it wisnae in Govan! Naw, my ma says there was this civil war in Spain years ago where aw these generals were puttin people in jail and torturin them. These generals were gettin help from Hitler but my ma says the British government did nothin so people came from aw ower tae help people fight back against the generals

Annie's by Andy Crichton

and the army. But it wisnae like it is now, just jump on a plane and you're there. Naw, it wis dangerous even tryin tae get there—you had tae get smuggled in. There wis guards everywhere. Think that's what happened tae my granda— got shot in the elbow crossin the border from France and so he had tae come back. Imagine goin aw that way and no bein able tae take part—must have been infuriatin!

Aye, it wis pretty terrible and it wisnae easy for him when he got back hame. Well obviously he couldnae work efter that—imagine tryin tae swing wan o they hammers wi that injury? That's right—nae chance! His sister helped look efter him—that wis Annie, so I suppose she'd have been my Great Aunt Annie. Naw, I never met her—bit of a shame cos she sounds really fascinating. She went away tae live in Canada, I think it wis. Well, she had a girlfriend y'see and, well, people weren't too sure about that sort o thing then. What? Aye, naw you're right, they're no actually smart about it the now either.

Anyway, she helped my granda look efter my ma when she wis wee and things like that. But here's a funny thing, right? Before that, my ma said wan o Annie's teachers wis in and out the jail aw the time and he thought his food wis bein poisoned so Annie used tae take food in for him. Naw, seriously, this happened, right—my ma says it wis way back in the twenties. He didnae seem like your average teacher—this guy used tae organise classes for people tae talk about economics and how the world wis run and stuff like that. He also spoke at big meetings—just like the ones they had at the shipyards if you see what I mean—and he wis sayin stuff like workin people shouldn't go tae war against each other. Now, what wis it he said: 'A bayonet is a weapon with a worker at each end'—dead clever that, is it no? Wish I could think o stuff like that. Anyway, the government didnae like him sayin stuff like that so he got the jail.

That's what my ma says as well—if aw the high heid yins are upset about something, put them in a field and let them sort it out amongst themselves! Shouldnae be workin people tae dae their fightin for them. Imagine that though—no think that's terrible? It's no right getting the jail for something like that—people are sayin stuff like that aw the time now. They're even making records about it—look at John Lennon for God's sake, aw that 'Merry Christmas war is over...' and he's no getting put in jail— although my da thinks he should!

Naw, so I'm no sure how Annie ended up doing that but my ma says that because the teacher thought the prison guards were poisoning his food, he went on hunger strike a coupla times. Aye, I know it sounds terrible. I think the suffragettes did the same thing. Jeez, could you do that, eh? Know ah couldnae!

Anyway, this guy was really, I mean really, popular, right? No wi the polis and the government and the judges—they couldnae stand him. My ma says they were actually aw scared o him. But the ordinary people, right? Well they really loved him—there wis loads o people turnin up for his classes and the streets were packed full when he wis speakin at wan o his meetings.

But there wis a coupla times in jail when he wis allowed tae have his own food brought in and that's how Annie got involved. My ma says it's because Annie had been a student o his so she got tae be wan o the people allowed tae bring food in—y'know, it had tae be someone he trusted tae do that.

Naw, don't know much more about the guy really—should ask my ma when she gets back in from her work, eh? Here's a thing—you think that using Annie would maybe be an awright example o somebody makin a difference? It aw sounds a bit brave and adventurous—no the sorta thing that ordinary wee Govan lassies usually get up tae, eh? You think so, aye? Right, need tae ask my ma then—find out a bit more about the guy and aw that.

Here, I wis wonderin—you think my teacher would know anything about him?

Jean Rafferty

is the author of three works of fiction, two books about sport and countless articles. As a journalist she was nominated twice for the UK Press Awards as feature writer of the year, an unusual honour for a freelance. She also won various awards, including a Joseph Rowntree journalist's fellowship for her work on prostitution. Her first two works of fiction were nominated for literary prizes, though she struggled to get a publisher for her third, *Foul Deeds Will Rise*, a novel about Satanist ritual abuse set in Orkney. It was published by Wild Wolf, an independent publisher from Newcastle. She and her five brothers and sisters grew up in a corporation flat in Glasgow, but her father was a teacher so she felt both working and middle class. She is chair of Scottish peace charity Dove Tales, the Association of Artists for Peace.

Didn't She Matter?

I knew the baby wasn't beside her when she died. It tormented me when I first read it; the thought of his chubby little hands reaching out to pat his mother or tug at her to give him food, only to find cold, waxy skin. The thought of him crying for her and no-one coming... I'd wake in the night thinking of him, not her. Maybe that's the way it should be, that we should focus on the living. But I couldn't let them say those things about her. Blessing would never have done anything bad round Gabriel. Just look at the pictures—he was a gorgeous, happy baby.

He was malnourished when they picked him up because he'd been on his own for so long, not because he was starving. Four days he was in his cot alone, with my poor, poor sister's body lying in the hallway.

They didn't tell us what had happened at first. I thought she must have killed herself because the people round about said it wasn't starvation, that she and Gabriel had food from the church and refugee charities. But it can't have been enough, can it? She had to write to some housing charity asking for help because she was struggling to survive. What kind of country tells someone they can't work after fourteen years? What was she supposed to do?

Didn't she matter?

I have the film of her on my phone. She looks so pretty, with her stripy trousers and two-tone shoes, thanking them for their kindness in bringing her food from home. A big bag of potatoes, some onions, rice? Very African. Oh yes, one big cassava. Perhaps there were plantains in the black plastic bag. I look and look and wonder how long it all lasted her.

I wish she'd told us she needed help. Maybe she was too proud. Or depressed. One of her friends said she wasn't herself towards the end—

—she was stressed about the immigration people, the quarrels with the handsome partner. I think of her in the shopping centre where the friend met her, a ghost of herself, haunting a world she didn't belong in. She had no money. Was she looking at food? Pretty things? Wondering if she had enough money to buy the alcohol that killed her in the end. She knew she had kidney and liver problems, that she shouldn't drink. She must have been desperate.

We don't want for money, we'd have looked after her. There was no need for charity. My father was a big politician, I'm a human rights lawyer, my brother's standing for office—do you think we're poor just because we're black? Blessing's partner Eric has a Masters in petroleum engineering but he couldn't help because he can't get a job in your country.

We were mortified when we heard she had to beg. How could she be living off other people when we have so many properties in Kampala, lots of land in our village? Have you seen where we live? We're in Ntinda, right next to Ministers' Village, where all the top men live—the politicians, the businessmen, the army chiefs. The foreign aid workers swanning around in their big four- wheel drives.

You're a rich country, so why do you make people like Blessing so unwelcome? Here in Uganda if a person comes seeking asylum they only have to wait three months for an answer. Three months. Blessing was in your country for fourteen years and you still couldn't say she was one of you?

I brought her here myself. She was going to study at a college in Scotland. My father said, 'You take her, Grace. It's too long a journey for her to be on her own.' She was always his baby. Mine too. My sister was only four when our mother died so I was the one who cared for her, who got her dressed in the morning, who told her about boys when she grew up.

The journey was a great adventure for us. Neither of us had been on an aeroplane before. As it rose high into the sky, we looked down on the low hills around Entebbe and felt we were a new kind of people. We were modern people who went to foreign countries and could be at home in any of them, sophisticated people with passports and suitcases with wheels on them.

Still, we kept the little packets of sugar left over from the flight and the plastic pots of butter, though the butter went rancid because we forgot all about it.

They said Glasgow was the second city of the Empire, but it seemed small compared to Kampala. The college was in an even smaller town next to it, Paisley, where they used to make shawls from that fancy Eastern pattern cowboys wear on their bandanas. Teardrops.

She could have stayed at home but there were no good jobs at that time so she came to Britain to better herself. You see? She was a worker, not some lazy, good-for-nothing who was trying to live off others. Even when they made her give up her job, she still worked as a volunteer in a charity shop.

She'd trained in social work, but the job she got was in an African café restaurant, the Calabash. I cried when I heard she would take leftover food home and share it with a friend while they watched a film together. We used to do that. We'd get a big plate of fried plantains and dip them into groundnut sauce while we sat on the sofa together, laughing at the Fockers or sighing over Brad Pitt in his black frock in Troy, though we liked Denzel even better.

I miss her.

I feel distracted all the time right now—I scraped my car in a traffic jam on Jinja Road the other day. And I'm angry. All these people using my sister's death for their politics. Saying she died of hunger. The system failed her. Even the First Minister of Scotland was talking about it, using it to blast English rules.

It's abuse. We're the ones grieving. We're the ones who've lost the person we love.

My father collapsed when he heard. We had to take him to the hospital. He's very frail now. I look at him going for his walk, hunched over, unsteady on his feet. Once he strode down the road as if he owned it. Now you could take him for an old homeless man, wandering with nowhere to go.

There were three hundred people at the funeral. That's how well respected we are, yet if we were in your country we'd be bottom of the heap, lower than the lowest class of drunks and homeless. That's what you do to immigrants, especially people with skin as dark as ours. Have you ever looked at us? Did you see how beautiful my sister was? A rainbow, her friend said, and she was right. I used to tease her about her purple lipsticks and scarlet nails, but they made me smile. At family parties she'd be the one the uncles and the teenage cousins flocked to—the flairboyant one, my auntie said.

I wanted her to be flairboyant. I knew the radiance inside her.

The journey home to Bugiri was long and hard. Father shivered in the air conditioning so we had to switch it off and the car was sweltering. Three hours in the hot sun with nothing to distract us from thoughts of Blessing. Dead...

Her baby alone. Four days alone, not knowing where his mother was...

The family began to gather almost as soon as we got there ourselves. It was too much for me, aunties wailing, cousins drinking and arguing. The coffin sitting there.

I went into the garden and leaned against the old jackfruit tree. The ripe fruit hung down, heavy with sorrow. I thought losing my mother was the worst thing that could happen in the world, but losing your sister is like losing part of yourself. You keep looking for her, expecting her to walk back in, shout out your name. Laugh.

The days of mourning seemed interminable, all the cooking, the relatives milling about the house. We're an important family—local people who worked on our farms walked for miles to bring us food, and always the friends and dignitaries arriving from the city in their air-conditioned SUVs. I wanted it to end.

On the afternoon when they laid her to rest I felt physically uncomfortable, as if I wasn't quite inhabiting my own body. They lifted Blessing from the coffin and lowered her into the ground, into the dirt. Some earth dislodged and fell on top of the body, instantly soiling her white shroud.

They started filling in the grave, shovelling soil on top of her. I could hardly breathe. They were suffocating my sister, burying her in the earth. She didn't belong there.

At night we lit the fire that would sweep Blessing's spirit away. As the flames crackled and flared upwards into the darkness, there was a roaring in my head—I didn't want her to be gone.

Gabriel should be with us. He is our blood, our kin. What kind of life will he have in your country, always at the bottom of the heap, always stared at for the colour of his skin. His father says he will play football for Scotland but why would he want that for his son, people making monkey noises at him? Do you think we don't know what goes on in your country?

Here he can do something useful, be a lawyer or a doctor or a minister.

I just want him here, want to hold him in my arms and make the world safe for him. I want to smother him with kisses, feel his baby arms round my neck... see my sister again in his smile.

Andrew O'Hagan

was born in Glasgow and grew up in Kilwinning, North Ayrshire. He is an internationally acclaimed novelist with three of his novels having been nominated for the Booker Prize for Fiction. He is also an editor—at-large for *The London Review of Books* and Visiting Professor of Writing at King's College, London. His latest novel is *Mayflies* and earlier this year he won the Christopher Isherwood Prize from the *Los Angeles Times*.

Cipher

'A dead man's corpse was worth fifty francs; but while alive, a man of talent without someone to push his interests, possessing not a single friend, sans mattress to lie on, was a useless burden to the State, a mere social cipher, unworthy of anyone's trouble.'

—Balzac, *The Fatal Skin*

That's a pure shame, so it is. Ma da's books. I only kept them because I couldnae stawn gawn doon tae the charity shoap. He'd underlined the words fae Balzac inside a copy he borrowed fae the libry. Naw, that's no right—it wisnae borrowed, he bote the book in wan ae they clearance sales, whidyecallthem, oan Saturday mornins. It said 'Govan Library—Cancelled' in big black letters as if the book hid loast its life. Bit in they days it wiz magic tae get cancelled, wint it? Mind? It wiz a relief, specially if it wiz a doacter's appointment, and noo its jeest somedy sayin the wrang word or ye know betrayin some weird prejudice and getting booted oot and that's them finished awthegither. Anywiy. Ma da wisnae the sorta guy who wid steal a book fae a public libry. Jesus. He wisnae even late wi eez libry books. That wiz ma da aw awr the back. Don't say he didnae dae his best because he did and that wiz jeest the stamp ae the man, at least tae me it wiz. Depends who ye listen tae. Ma maw iywiz sayed he couldni stick in wan place and wiz iywiz ready for the off.

I put doon the book and left the hoose. The door banged shut. It wisnae supposed tae dae that; it wiz meant tae wait tae yi loaked it wi the key. I goat a joiner oot tae fix it wan time and ye know what the cheeky bastart did? He spent an oor and a hawf dayin nuthin, and then he goes tae me, 'You wouldni wahnt tae be loakin yersel oot, hen,' and then he goes lit at wi a hammer. Bangs the hing twice. Bloody useless. That wiz in Decemba. I pide him cash-in-hand and the door's still broke. Cowboys, some ae thum.

Go'n doon in the lift I thote tae masel, see that guy, see every guy lit at. They should be pide aff or made tae answer tae the people they've let doon. It's ordinary people they're messin aboot and they hink they're that fly. Stoap it.

Sometimes you neetae have a word wi yersel.

I told masel years ago no tae get angry in the lifts. Use the lift, I said tae masel, tae get calm and coont doon tae the loaby—easy diz it, but dae it.

I love ma wee motor, so a dae. It's ma wee haven. Drivin up Hillingdon Road tae ma work you come tae Burger King at the roundaboot and I iywiz stoap there for a roll and a cuppa tea if I've goat time. I jeest sit in the motor blowin intae the cup. I dunno whit it is aboot Burger King but they make their tea too warrum. It's handy for Farmfoods anaw at that roundaboot so I iywiz look forward tae it, getting a few messages efter ma tea and jeest feeling you've goat time tae yersel—know whit a mean?—before your shift. So I'm gawn, 'Aye, right. I'm sure'n I'll be hurryin masel tae get tae the wards early when I'm oan nights.' But eventually I shoved the wrapper intae the cup and walked acroass the corpark.

Right next tae the skip, a man's lyin there wi nuthin oan. Quite a young man tae wi his eyes shut and no a mark oan him at aw. Jeest lyin. I looked ower ma shooder but there wiz naebdy aboot and I didnae really know whit tae dae. I shouldny say it, a wummin ae ma age, and a nurse tae, but he wiz beautiful lyin there. Beautiful brown skin he hud and no a mark oan him like I say and jeest this peaceful look oan his face. He wiz trim and a teeny wee ant came up his airm and marched ower eez stomach. You go intae action stations, daint ye? I bent doon and took iz pulse and then orr tae the shoap and sayz tae the wummin behin the coonter there wiz a guy outside by the bins wi nae claes oan. Unconscious, like. Jeest lyin there as if he'd drapped fae the sky. She looked at me as if I wiz daft and so I went back tae the motor and goat ma phone and rang an ambulance.

They took um tae oor hospital, Queen Elizabeth's. I don't work in the accident and emergency department and I never saw him agane that efternin, but aboot ten a'cloak that night, during ma brek, I wandered doon and fun um in the ICU. I hudnae known the ambulance guys but I telt them whit I knew when they picked um up. Since then, the doacters hudnae been able tae wake him and the polis were lookin at the CCTV and aw that. Wan ae them said there wiz nothing there. Zilch. It didnae show the guy turnin up in the corpark or getting chased or anyhin. It wiz like he'd been dumped oot ae a motor or he jeest appeared oot ae thin air and they wur totally stumped, so they wur. A doacter came alang the corridor tae the nurses' station, and, it's like, there's nuthin tae identify the bloke, no even a phone or a travel document or a ring or anyhin. They said he hud a wee scar by his right eye, and another, like, another scar oan his side. It's hard intit tae tell somebdy's story bi a few scars.

We never saw people nakeit when I wiz young. I'm serious: he's deed noo, but I never saw ma da withoot his claes oan, nor ma maw. You must be kiddin. Even runnin fae the bathroom tae the bedroom wi a towel wrapped roon them; they would've warned you they were coming, so's you could jump behin a door or whatever, know whit a mean? The only body we ever saw wiz oan the big croass at the back of St John Ogilvie's. Huge hing. Jesus wi his ribs stickin oot and a cloth ower, you know, aw that, and his eyes upturned that wiy, blood—or red paint I suppose it wiz—streaking doon his airms and feet. I wiz iy that bored at Mass, I would stare at his knees and imagine talkin tae him at the bus stoap, like he wiz an ordinary bloke. My auntie Audrey used tae go intae pure raptures jeest talkin aboot Jesus oan the croass. Wan time the alarm cloak in her haunbag went oaf during Mass and we aw looked roon and it wiz as if Jesus up there wiz rollin iz eyes at her wi aw her daft kerry-oan.

The guy didnae huv a name, so they didnae know whit tae dae wi him, basically. His vital signs were aw normal and they put him intae a room nearer us. Turns oot the polis sayed he wiz mibbe an asylum-seeker because of the CCTV at the bus station. But that didnae explain how he ended up wi nuthin oan, an nae cards, nae phone nor nuthin. Wheniver I came doon he wiz by eezsel and he hid a drip gawn, oxygen at 98, pulse steady. The lassies aw laughed at me but I said it wiz a pure shame, a nice guy lit at. Nae name. For a whole week I looked forward tae seein um and hoped he wid wake up and tell us eez story. I wahntid tae tell um aboot the Jesus statue at the back ae the church where we used tae stiy, and aboot my auntie Audrey's alarm cloak, but he didnae budge aw week.

'He's a transitional nobody,' a consultant said, examining eez chart and tappin it wi a pen. 'He'll soon be returned.'

'But mibbe he hiz a faimly,' I said. 'Jeest lit us. Mibbe he stiys here. Do you think he'll speak lit us when he wakes up?'

'He won't be here long.'

'How no?'

'He's not our problem.'

I love ma wee motor and the sound it makes startin. Jeest the fact that it's iywiz ready tae take me where I wahnt tae go. When am in the corpark at the Burger King I iywiz think ae the bloke I found lyin by the skip. He goat tangled up in ma mind wi the hing ma da underlined in that book fae the libry and you don't forget they wee hings, dae ye? You don't let them pass you by and yit they're disappearing aw the time.

Jim Aitken

Little Scots Words

Lately, Lynda had taken to reminiscing as she sat down after her tea. Her mother had warned her against this. *'You will have plenty to do all day in the house,'* she would say, *'that you will be too tired at night for anything else. And you have the garden to look after as well.'*

If only, thought Lynda.

When her father had died she and her brother Gus had watched their mum go into overdrive cleaning, washing, ironing and having Gus re-paint the entire house for her on a yearly basis. But Lynda was not her mother, Trisha. Clearly she had similar traits and found that housework achieved certain things. It gave you comfortable surroundings to live in a house that was yours to admire, but such labour could not take away the sense of deep loss she had at the passing of her husband, Jim.

She had been retired for close on ten years now and with their three girls all away, she and Jim had looked forward to their autumnal years together, travelling and looking after their grandchildren whenever they were called upon. She would often sit in the evenings now, waiting for the distant flashes from her past to visit her.

Two nights ago it was the memory of her first week teaching, way back in 1978. She was Lynda Keneally then, and within a year she would be Mrs Munro. She was the first from her housing scheme in Edinburgh's Moredun to go to university, and coming from a working-class background made her conscious of that background in a staff-room that was largely different to her own. Yet, here she was in a large comprehensive secondary school at the western edge of the city and the voices of the students were not too unlike the sound of her own voice.

A week after starting her probationer year of teaching, she came upon the Deputy Head, Mr Duguid, remonstrating with a third-year boy in one of the corridors.

'Did you wilfully refuse to leave the room when Miss Ingram told you to do so?' asked the tall figure of Mr Duguid, looking down at the boy with his penetrating stare.

'Naw, ah didnae. She didnae gie me enough time,' replied the hapless boy.

'I shall re-phrase this in the plainest of English. Did you refuse to leave the class when Miss Ingram told you?'

'Ah've awready tellt ye. She didnae gie me enough time.'

The boy was certainly holding his own, thought Lynda. She had a

178

sneaking admiration for his stand, and this grew as Mr Duguid continued with his pompous questioning.

'*I take it you are a member of Miss Ingram's S3 English class?*'

'*Aye,*' was the monosyllabic response.

'*Do you mean to say yes? Is that what you are inferring by such an utterance?*' Mr Duguid was now flustered and losing his composure as Lynda kept her distance round the corner.

'*Aye, ah am,*' said the boy without being fully aware that Mr Duguid was now engaged in attacking his Scots tongue. Whatever had happened in the classroom had become something entirely different, and at that moment Lynda stepped out into the fray. She approached Mr Duguid with a few quick steps and said to him with wide-open eyes, '*Mr Duguid, if aye is good enough for the House of Commons, it is certainly good enough for this Scottish school.*'

Mr Duguid was aghast, but understood exactly what she was getting at. He simply walked away and left her with the boy who thought he was going to be reported to the House of Commons.

'*Look, son,*' she said to him, '*when a teacher tells ye tae leave the room, ye leave it. Got it?*' asked Lynda with her heart pounding, but her mind still resolute.

'*Aye, miss,*' said the boy, with all his earlier defiance washed away as he looked at Miss Keneally.

'*Right, then. Get back in there and say sorry to Miss Ingram.*'

'*Yes, Miss,*' the boy replied, leaving Lynda amazed that she had elicited a yes from the boy when it had not been sought.

Last night she thought of Jim. They were on holiday together in Ibiza, in one of the quiet parts, away from all the crazed clubbers. He had this incredible stabbing pain in his back and he was never usually one to moan about things. Nothing seemed to relieve the pain either, but he bravely put up with it until they got back home.

It was bad news. Jim seemed to deteriorate quickly after the diagnosis, and she shared every last moment with him. He had said to her with his soft voice, '*Nae greetin, mind.*' Those three words like the words he once said to her before they got married—'*Ah love you*'—were words that had entered her being, never to leave her until she left herself.

As if she could not cry for the husband she had spent so many happy years with; as if she could not cry for their three girls Caitlin, Roisin and Niamh he had loved and were now without their father; and as if she could not cry for the grandchildren they both loved who will grow up without him.

Nae greetin, mind—it was just like Jim to come out with something like that. He knew as she knew that he was passing away, and to have come out with that at the end was so beautifully Scottish, with all the tenderness and compassion he could muster in those three such simple words. None of that overblown, flowery language that never penetrates the heart. Three simple words that said so much and came back to her last night and would do so for many more nights to come.

Another flash of distant memory visited Lynda, and she could see Jim heading off with Siobhan and Sinead for a walk in their double buggy. He had looked forward to being retired after all those years working as a plumber, and these grandchildren were just what he needed at this stage of his life. Caitlin had dropped them off, and Jim was delighted to see his grandchildren. His words that day were—'*and how are these bonnie wee bairns?*' Their eyes lit up at this, and they knew they were in for a good time. Caitlin had things to do that day, and Lynda had arranged to see her mother and she could remember the smile on Jim's face as he was getting the twins to himself.

The words—*bonnie wee bairns*—were so full of the innocence, the fragility and vulnerability we associate with little children. A bairn is more than a child. A child is too technical and too exact to capture that special period of early life. *Pretty little children* simply does not cut it, thought Lynda. She had campaigned in her union and sat on committees to promote Scots and eventually she would win through when Scottish writers were used to study for examinations, but that was a good while ago now. Though she had been an English teacher who loved Shakespeare, she had that sense of mission towards Scots that probably came from speaking it when she was young, hearing and using words like *cannae, shouldnae, willnae, huvnae, gonnae, disnae, dinnae* and so many more besides. She had loved the rhythmic sound the words made, and the naturalness of the words became part of her until her own schooling tried to change all that.

Caitlin, Roisin and Niamh were her own *bonnie wee bairns* even though they were grown up adults now, but she could remember them when they were young as if it were yesterday. And she realised that her yesterdays were full of little Scots words that had been used when English ones could not do it. *Aye* and *naw* were more expressive than *yes* or *no*, which seemed somehow more clinical. And nothing could compare with *nae greetin, mind.* If Jim had said to her that day *no crying, remember* she would never have remembered those words. They could never have penetrated her the way Jim said *nae greetin, mind.* And to say greet is to conjure powerful, tearful emotion that creates tracks down the face for tears to travel.

All languages are wonderful, mused Lynda. They are wonderful because they come from all the places where all the ordinary people who first used these words lived, and that was why she supported Gaelic, even though she knew only a handful of words in that language that sounded like the wind and the sea and the rain. English too was one of those lovely languages, but these past nights it was the little Scots words that were so sharp and sweet and broke the heart.

Leela Soma

was born in Madras, India, and now lives in Glasgow. Her poems and short stories have been published in several anthologies and publications. She has published three novels, short stories, a chapbook & two collections of poetry. She was also nominated for the Pushcart Prize 2020. She has been appointed Scriever 2021 for the Federation of Writers (Scotland). She has been added to the Scottish Poetry Library's guide of poets, and last year she had two poems included in *A Kist of Thistles*. Some of her work reflects her dual heritage of India and Scotland. The following story was first published in *The Scotsman*. Her website address is leelasoma.wordpress.com

Locked In
(India, 1889)

'It is compassion, the most gracious of virtues,
which moves the world.'

—Thiruvalluvar, *Kural* (5th century CE)

I pondered on these words I had heard at the temple. The sages say such wise things that are easy to listen to but hard to practise in life. I looked up at the dark sky. The moon was but a small crescent as I walked back to my silent home, drowned in grief. My daughter was dying. No words could soothe me.

A week later, it was all over. I walked for miles in the village outside the cantonment. I had just cremated my young daughter that day. Consumption, said the doctor. I had watched as her body wasted away and life had left her thin frame. I was bereft.

As I took a turn near the bushes, I heard someone sobbing their heart out.

'What's up? What's this crying for?' I asked gently.

A young girl scrambled to her feet. She looked scared.

'Aren't you *Tubal*'s daughter?'

She nodded. Her shoulders shook with sobs. She wiped her tears.

'My pass... they took it off me. I failed the medical test. They said this disease can't be cured now.' Tears streamed again, and her throat caught a sob.

'I have nowhere to go. I can't go back to my house. How will I live?' she whispered.

She was no more than fourteen or fifteen, a young girl with a child-like face. My heart went out to her. I could not think straight.

'It is dark. I don't know where to go,' she whispered. Her sobs were muffled by the hem of the sari that she used to cover her mouth.

'Come with me. I'll do what I can,' I said, seeing her body tremble.

Under the cover of darkness, I smuggled her into the cowshed in the cantonment. I let her sleep there. I was a bearer who had looked after the Sahib for years. This was in Saugaor, a cantonment under the Bombay command of a British regiment. As soon as the cantonment was ready for the thousand plus soldiers, quarters were set aside for twelve or fourteen young Indian women to service them.

When I told my wife, she screamed obscenities.

'Don't you dare get involved with that filthy girl! What if the Sahib finds out? You'll lose your job. Think of us first.' She shivered with fright and anger. 'Have you gone out of your mind? We have just lost our child...?

Her anguish rent my heart.

Before the first sound of dawn, I hurried to the cowshed. I woke the girl and we walked on quietly, until we came to the river. She washed her face and drank some water.

'*Pushpa*, that's my name. I am the youngest of six children.'

Her name meant flower. Yes, she did look delicate, I thought to myself. Like my girl who had faded away from life.

'Where are we going?' she asked.

She squatted on the ground and cried, refusing to follow me. Vulnerable and limp as the faded flowers on the dusty tree beside the road, she slumped forward.

I helped her up. 'Wait here under the shade of the tree. I'll get you something to eat.'

I rushed over to the nearest chai shack and bought her a clay pot of tea.

Nirmal, the chaiwallah, stirred the old urn and poured me a cup. I asked him for some old *parathas.* He packed it in the dried leaves that he kept for taking food away, and joked: 'Hey, you are up early! So *bibi* didn't cook for you today? Why are you in such a hurry? Sahib whipping you again?'

I nodded a quick yes and ran back. We sat by the old ruins near the river. I watched as she ate the parathas hungrily and downed the *chai* in one gulp.

'You know all I wanted in life was to have enough to eat, maybe some coloured bangles and a nice sari.' She cried and recalled her horrific life.

'Now I'm nothing, forced into something I never wanted. I can't go back to the village.'

'No, you are just a child. I'll do what I can to help you. Just stay out of sight.' I hurried home.

*

I worked all day, polishing his shoes, getting his clothes ready, waiting on him hand and foot. He was in a bad temper all day, sitting at his desk, flipping pages of reports and shouting out commands to the junior officers. He drank more than usual and whipped me for forgetting to refill his glass at lunch time. The afternoon siesta gave me a brief respite, but soon it was tiffin time and I was busy.

Later, as the darkness fell, and the moon rose in the sky, the stars twinkled and I thought again of that poor child *Pushpa*, hiding in the old ruins. The Sahib was in a foul mood. He had more *chota* pegs all day.

Sahib's beautiful bungalow was lit up with lamps and I could see the crystal glasses glinting in the light as I stood beside the *punkah wallah*, in the doorway of the room, hot and sweating in the humid night air. Sahib was drinking with the bigger Sahib. They were looking at papers and talking animatedly. Every time I went in to pour the drinks or clear the snacks and take a fresh batch in, I caught bits of the conversation. Their voices were rising.

'Bloody mess, that's what I call it. Who would print a copy of Lord Robert's Memorandum?' bellowed the big Sahib.

'And give a copy to each and every Member of Parliament?'

My Sahib's eyes were bloodshot.

'Now all this debate about repealing the Cantonments Act! They have no bloody idea of our lives in this hell-hole.'

'All for these stupid whores! The Government set up the Lock Hospitals and now they want to close them. Diseases will spread like wild fire.'

'Not been the same since the Mutiny. These natives are getting restless. No one in London understands!'

They drank more, eyeing me as I poured the spirits into their glasses.

'Bloody Liberals, they sit in England and make the bloody rules. They wouldn't last a few months in this god-forsaken country!'

I polished the decanter. Lock Hospitals, that's where *Pushpa* had said she was examined and thrown out because she had some disease. I knew of the girls kept in the hospital, under lock and key and getting caught if they escaped. One girl was fined five rupees by the Magistrate Sahib. Where could she get that kind of money? No one ever saw her again. No one could stay inside the cantonment without passes. My mind was working fast on how I could help *Pushpa*.

The smell of night jasmine arose in the night air. I breathed in a lungful.

'Bearer, where the hell are you, *jaldi*?' Sahib's loud voice shook me; his red face loomed in front of me. I ran in and refilled their glasses.

I strained my ears again. What were they talking about? I couldn't understand some of it. But they mentioned that the *kutwal* needed to be sent again for more fresh girls, and that till the law was repealed they would carry on as usual.

It was late when I went back to the ruins. She was asleep and woke up terrified when I called her name in the dark. I told her that there was little I could do to get her back to the cantonment or get her help in any other way. The Sahib was not someone I could even talk to as he was drunk with anger and gin.

I kept asking around. What happens to the girls thrown out of the cantonment? The others just laughed; they cared little.

Nirmal, the chaiwallah, was more forthcoming. I had quite a few chats with him.

'Why, are you involved with one of those?' he asked smirking and winking.

'No, no, of course not,' I said.

'Then forget the whores. Nobody wants them. They get thrown out because they get these terrible diseases from the Sahibs. You know I've been working in this same shack for twenty years now. That cantonment has been good for my business. But the poor girls have had a horrible time. You know the kutwal, that Bal Singh, he is the one who goes around with the two policemen and selects new girls from the village for that place. Shame these *goras* didn't bring their own women.'

Pushpa stayed in the ruins. The river gave her fresh water and she had shade to sleep in. She begged for food when I couldn't smuggle any food to her. She looked thin and emaciated and my heart churned each time I saw her. I felt guilty when I came home to comfort. My heart twisted with pain.

Nirmal chatted as he sipped his *chai.*

'Have you seen these *goras* talking to the village women and helping them, even the whores? They wear those ghost like clothes, covering their heads, and they carry those books and a cross always.' He shook his head in disapproval.

'Oh, those nuns from the American mission? I saw them when I took the Memsahib to the church the other day. She wanted me to carry a big parcel of old curtains for their charity.'

I set off next day when I was free. I stood at the door of this huge church. I heard some strange songs in a different language. I waited a long time.

A nun passed me by. I cleared my throat.

'Memsahib, can I ask you to help me?'

'What is it? Do you have a message from your Sahib?'

'No, no... there is a young girl, *Pushpa...*' I hesitated.

'Yes?'

'She is unwell, has no pass and has been thrown out of the cantonment.' I explained *Pushpa's* plight.

She asked me to wait there.

In a few minutes two other nuns came along and asked me more details. One of them wrote down on a paper as I spoke.

'Please. I don't want to lose my job. My Sahib would be very angry if he finds out about this.'

'Don't worry. Bring her to us as soon as you can. Go. Hurry! We can help.'

I was so relieved and happy that I fell at their feet and prostrated myself.

I rushed over and brought *Pushpa* to them. They took us to a room in a small building near the church. There were three other girls like *Pushpa*, squinting on the floor. They had a cross in their hand and were repeating something like a mantra.

'We will take care of her, you go home. She has come to God,' the nuns told me.

I walked back home slowly.

Source: The National Library of Scotland has a set of papers on the Medical History of British India.

Glossary of Hindi words

bibi—Miss, *chaiwallah*—tea seller, *chota pegs*—half measure of whisky, *goras*—white people, *jaldi*—hurry, fast, *kutwal*—Police Chief, *paratha*—flatbread, *punkah wallah*—manual fan operator, Sahib—master

James Robertson

is a poet, fiction writer and editor. Born in Kent, he has lived in Scotland from the age of six. He studied history at Edinburgh University and worked in various jobs, including eight years as a bookseller, before becoming a full-time writer. From 1993 to 1995 he was writer-in-residence at Brownsbank Cottage near Biggar, the former home of Hugh MacDiarmid, whose work had already influenced his attitudes to language, literature and politics. He has written six novels, including *Joseph Knight*, *The Testament of Gideon Mack* and *And the Land Lay Still*. He is a co-founder of and contributing editor to Itchy Coo, a Scots language imprint for young readers, and believes that Scots is an integral and vital element of Scottish culture. His latest novel, *News of the Dead*, is published in 2021.

Unsicht
(A free translation of *L'Aveugle* by Guy de Maupassant)

Whit is it, in the spring, that maks that first blink o sun sae braw? When that licht faws on ye, dae ye no jist full up wi the sense that life is guid? The sky's aw blue, the land green, the hooses white; and yir een sook in aw thae colours and yir lugs aw the soonds o life, and yir sowl itsel taks wing like a laverock. And yir hail ingyne is kittled up: ye want tae dance, tae run, tae sing, there's a lichtsomeness in ye, a warmth and tenderness that spreids oot tae awbody. Ye feel ye could gie the sun itsel a kiss and a smoorich.

But whit aboot the blin men? Whit dae they feel? They staun as they aye dae at the mooths o closes, their faces steekit in ayebidin nicht. They're lown and passive in the minds o aw this new energy, and they're aye sootherin their dugs as if they dinna ken jist why the beasts should be sae fretful and yivverie.

When they gang hame at the day's end, mibbe cleekin on tae the airm o a wee brither or sister that's been sent tae convoy them, if the bairn says, 'Whit a braw day it's been!' they say, 'Aye, I thocht it must be. Luath widna bide still for a meenit.'

I'm gaun tae tell ye aboot yin o these sichtless men, whase life wis yin o the sairest trauchles ye could iver imagine.

A peasant he wis, a fermer's laddie oot awa frae the city. As lang as his faither and mither were alive, he didna fair ower badly: aw he'd tae thole wis his unsicht. But, whenever the auld folk passed ower, that's when the horror begun for him. He wis taen in by a sister, on a ferm whaur awbody treated him like a scunge or a scrounger for eatin the breid that ithers had tae warsle tae provide. Ilka meal wis begrugdit him; they cried him an eejit and a wastrel; and even though his guid-brother had swicked him o his pairt o the heritance, they were sweer tae gie him even a bowlie o broth, and even

187

then ainly jist eneuch tae keep him frae stervin.

His face wis geyan gash, and his twa muckle een were white as kirk wafers; and he tholed aw the insults wi a siccar mooth and a stieve face, sae that naebody could tell if he wis hurtit by them. He'd niver kent muckle kindness: even his ain mither had aye been sherp wi him, no shawin him ony real love; for if a man cannae dae his share o the work in the fields whit use is he? Peasant folk spare nae sentiment on sic matters. They admire the hens in the yaird, that hae a peckin order and whiles kill aff the weakest amang them, for the guid o the tribe.

Efter he'd had his broth, he'd awa and sit oot at the door in simmer, in at the lum in winter, and he widna shift tae the forenicht. He widna move, he widna speak; but aye the blinnerin lids o his een wid be flickerin ower the whiteness ablow. Whit wis he thinkin? Did he hae ony sense at aw whit his life wis aboot? Naebody could be fashed tae fin oot.

That wis hoo it wis for a hantle years. But the fact that he couldna dae ocht, as weel as the fact that naethin seemed tae pit him up nor doon, turnt his faimly frae him. He became the butt o their gecks and jamphs, a kind o gowk-mairtyr, a prap for whitiver they ettle tae fling at him.

There wis nae limit tae the cruelties that his unsicht inspired in them. Tae compensate for whit he ate, they made his meals intae entertainments: oors o agony for him, oors o pleisure for the neebors.

Folk frae the nearhaun clachans cam by tae jine in the fun; wurd gaed frae door tae door, and the ferm kitchen wis fair chokit wi bodies ilka day. Whiles, a cat or a dug wid be pit on the table, in front o the bowl that he wis tae tak his soup frae. The beast's ain ingyne tellt it that the man couldna see, and it wid sleekitly draw near, makkin nae soond, and cannily lap at the soup; and if an unco loud plash o its tung alerted the puir deil, it wid wicely retreat in order tae jouk the wild skelp that he'd mak at it wi his spune.

Syne there wid be hootin and dunchin and rampin o bitts frae the onlookers reenged the lenth o the waw. And himself, athoot a wurd, wid stert tae eat yince mair wi his richt haun, while wi his left airm he tried tae guaird and bield his plate.

At ither times they pit corks in his soup, dauds o widd, leaves and griss; even keech, that crottled awa sae he couldna pick it oot.

Syne, they wearied o their ploys; and the guid-brither, mad that he wis ayewis haein tae feed the craitur, took tae batterin him, lounderin him athoot mercy and lauchin at his useless ettlen tae jouk the blaws or hit back. Sae this wis the new gemm: the gemm o skelps, blin man's buff wi a real blin man. The ploomen, the orramen and the kitchie deems wid pit their hauns richt in at his face, and this stertit the blinnerin movement o his ee-lids. He didna ken whaur the nixt scud or sclaff wid come frae, and had tae keep his airms streetched oot aw the time tae fend aff their hits at him.

Efter aw this, they gart him beg. They set him oot at the roadside on mercat days, and whenever he heard a body gang past or the rackle o a coach, he wis tae haud oot his bunnet and caw, 'Spare ony chynge, please?'

But fermers are no rife wi their siller, and for hail weeks he didna bring hame a bawbee.

Sae at last wis unyokit him a hatred that wis athoot ony trace o pity. And this brings me tae the mainner o his daith.

It wis winter, and the grund wis happit ower wi snaw, and it froze wi a dour and terrible hardness. His guid-brither, this ae morning, took him a lang gait tae a main road, and left him tae cadge frae onybody that micht pass by. He left him there aw day, but when he gaed back in the gloaming he said he wisna able tae find him. 'Ach, but we'll no fash,' he said. 'Somebody'll hae taen him in because he wis cauld. He's aye been guid at makkin folk feel sorry for him! He'll turn up the morn's morn for his soup, see if he disna.'

But the morn's morn, he didna kythe.

I doot the wey it fell oot wis this. Efter waitin for oors, grippit ticht wi the cauld, and feeling himself shuttin doon and daith hotchin aboot him, the blin man wid hae begun tae walk. No able tae feel the road, which wis unner a scruif o ice, he'd hae wanered aw weys, stoitin and staucherin, pitchin intae sheuchs and sclimmin back oot, getting himself on his feet, settin aff yince mair, aye haudin forrit, aye getting naewhaur, aye silent in the toom silence aw roonaboot him, as he socht a hoose or ony kind o bield for the nicht.

But there wis nane, and bit by bit the lourdness o the snaw invadit him, and his dwaiblie legs couldna cairry him ony further, and he sat doon in the mids o a field. And he didna heeze himself up again.

The bonnie white flichans fell athoot cease and smoored him. His shilpit body wis buried ablow the deepinin snaw; and there wis naethin tae tell whaur the corpse lay.

For a hail eicht days his faimly made a muckle shaw o spieren efter him and lookin for him. They even grat for him.

It wis a roch, dour winter and the thaw wis lang in comin. But, a Sunday cam when the fermers, on their wey tae kirk, saw a muckle flock o craws turnin and hingin ower this ae field, drappin doon like a black plump o rain, syne risin again, drappin and risin, and ayewis returnin tae the same spot.

The week efter they were aye there, thae thrawn, dreich birds, a great cloud o them that seemed tae hae gaithered frae aw the airts; and they drapped doon wi muckle skreichs intae the skinklan snaw, makkin a weird pattern o a kaleidoscope ainly wi nae colours.

A laddie gaed ower tae see whit they were aboot, and fund whit remained o the body o the blin man, hauf eaten. His sichtless een were awready awa, pykit oot by the lang, sherp nebs o the stervin craws.

And I can niver experience the braw bricht days o spring, athoot sparin a thocht for that puir freenless sowl. Nor can I pit frae my mind whit his faimly used tae say: sae sad and sair had his life been on account o his unsicht that, horrible though it wis tae think on it, his daith wis a mercy and a solace tae awbody that had kent him.

Glossary of Scots Words

aw the airts—all directions
aw weys—all over the place
ayebidin—perpetual
ayewis—always
bield—protect, shelter
blinnerin—rapidly moving
broo—job centre
bunnet—cap
clachans—hamlets
cleekin—clutching
crottled—crumbled
dauds o widd—pieces of wood
deil—devil
dominie—teacher
doot—think, suspect
doucely—gently
dowp—bottom
dreich—dismal
dumfounert—dumbfounded
dunchin—nudging, elbowing
dwaiblie—feeble
dwaum—daydream
een—eyes
eejit—idiot
ettled—aimed, intended
ettlin—attempted
fashed—bothered
feart—afraid
flichans—snowflakes
forenent—in front of
forenicht—evening
forrit—forward
gart—forced
gash—dismal, ghastly
gecks—jibes
geyan—somewhat
girss—grass
gloaming—twilight
gowk—fool
grat, greet—wept, cry

guid-brither—brother-in-law
hail—whole
a hantle—a few
happit ower—covered over
heeze—raise
hotchin—hovering
ilka—every
ingyne—intellect, sense of being
jamphs—jokes
jouk—dodge
keech—excrement
kittled up—stimulated
kythe—appear
laldy—with gusto
a lang gait—a long distance
laverock—skylark
lounderin—beating
lourdness—heaviness
lown—calm
lugs—ears
lum—chimney
mankiest—dirtiest
maw—mother
mercat—market
mingin—bad smelling
muckle—big, much
nearhaun—nearby
nebs—beaks
offy—off license
ocht—anything
orramen—odd-job man
plump—heavy downpour
poindings—sale of household goods to pay rent
prap—target
puir—poor
rackle—rattle
rampin—stamping
reenged—spread out
roch—rough
sair—sore, hard
sair wecht—a burden, struggle
sclaff—slap

sclimmin—climbing
scruif—layer, crust
scud—blow
scunge—one who slinks about
scunner—irritant
sheuchs—ditches
shilpit—emaciated
shuin—shoes
siccar—firm, fixed
siller—money
skelf—splinter
skelp—blow
skinklin—glittering
skreichs—screeches
smoored—smothered
smoorich—embrace
sook—suck
sootherin—soothing
spierin—asking
staucherin—staggering
steekit—shut up
stieve—stiff, set
stottin—tripping
stravaiging—wandering
sweer—reluctant
syne—then
tak tent—take care
tashes—spots
tentie—caring
thae—those
thirled—bound
thole—endure
thrang—throng, crowd
thrawn—persistent
toom—empty
trauchles—trials
unco—unusually
unsicht—lack of sight
unyokit—unleashed
warsle—struggle
waw—wall
wean—child

wheesht—be quiet
whiles—sometimes
wicely—discreetly
yince mair—once more
yivverie—quivering with excitement